So, You Wanna Be a Travel Nurse?

ISBN: 978-1-7365855-0-4 (Paperback)
ISBN: 978-1-7365855-1-1 (E-book)

Library of Congress Control Number: 2021902124

Cover Design	Dionisio C. Manalo, Jr.
Interior Design	Olivier Darbonville
Photos of Author	Joey Michel Photography

SO, YOU WANNA BE A
TRAVEL NURSE?

AN INSIDER'S GUIDE TO GETTING STARTED

Constance Buccere
MSN, RN, CCRN-CMC-CSC

Contents

FOR BRENDA

_Thank you for setting this in motion years ago,
when you gave me the idea to write a book
about my travel nursing journey._

Preface

WHEN I'M ASKED, "HOW LONG HAVE YOU BEEN traveling?" my answer, "ten years," since I started this journey in fall of 2011. But the truth is, I started *travel nursing* four years earlier in the summer of 2007 during my undergraduate nursing program, when I did a study abroad program in Honduras. I spent two weeks learning and providing nursing care with a team of eight American nursing students in undergraduate or graduate school, several Honduran nursing students, and three Honduras-based physicians in Tegucigalpa, Talanga, Guiamaca, and Roatán. I learned a lot about myself, the areas I needed to work on, as a student nurse before transitioning into a practicing registered nurse (RN), and that travel was coded in my DNA.

I spent the first few years of my career bouncing from specialty to specialty, feeling restless and unfulfilled. I love what I do, but at the time I just didn't feel challenged, leading me to take a job as a neuroscience outcomes analyst at the hospital where I was working. I completed research that was later turned into *Hardwiring Best Practice Stroke Care,* a presentation about implementing the American Stroke Association's guidelines for emergency and inpatient stroke care, but this wasn't cutting it either. I was still feeling restless. Then one day in the spring of 2011, the lightbulb started shining bright during a conversation with a colleague. I was talking about looking for another position because I was bored. She pointed out that I changed jobs every few months and that wouldn't look good on a résumé for the future. As she held that mirror up, reflecting my behavior, I thought back to a travel nurse I met during my first job as a RN. She talked about 13-week contracts, moving all over the country for work, and taking a month off every year. As the conversation about my behavior ended, I realized I was a travel nurse, just in one hospital. And that was the beginning of a career that has given me more than I could have ever imagined. I don't think I ever thanked my colleague for that, but I'm grateful, even though I wasn't at the time.

After a few years as a travel nurse, I would get asked about getting started in the industry by staff nurse colleagues. I would give them the agency and hospital interview questions and some of the guidance in this book to help them. As this pattern repeated, several nurses said I should write a book about getting started in travel nursing. This would trigger the memory of the first time I heard I should write a book about travel nursing that came from my therapist in late 2012. I remember thinking *this woman is crazy,* but truthfully, she was just the first to see what the nurses telling me to write a book also saw. The more I heard this, the more I started to believe that I could and should write about what I knew. Finally, in September 2019, the planets aligned, and everything clicked.

While I continued to work 36-hour a week travel contracts, I would write bits of this book between enjoying the attractions and fun of my assignments' destinations. While working an assignment in California, the coronavirus pandemic hit, shutting down everything, leaving me with nowhere to go and nothing to do except work. My contract for CVICU was transitioned to COVID ICU because heart surgeries were canceled, except for emergencies. Working in a COVID ICU before we knew the basics of the virus and how to treat it took a mental and emotional toll. I saw more death in three months than I had in the previous 12 years of being a nurse. The only mental stress relief working for me was being outside, walking and biking through the neighborhood. Then came the wildfires from an August thunderstorm, forcing me to be inside, creating the perfect storm for a breakdown.

After my breakdown or coming-to-terms with life, as my best friend referred to it, I focused my energy on this book, which only took three to four months to get on the page so my editors could make it the best for you, dear reader. Thank you for your time and dime; I hope this book gives you the foundation for starting a great career in travel nursing, however long you plan to do it, and don't forget ... *Enjoy the journey.*

—

Is Travel Nursing Right for You?

Are you independent? Do you like to chal-lenge yourself personally and professionally? Do you have an adventurous spirit or a touch of wanderlust? Are you up for an adventure that allows you to meet new people and experience new places and cultures in a way that you can't with a traditional vacation? Can you quickly adapt? Are you able to handle changing environments every few months? If you answered "no" to any of these questions, put the book down now. Close the cover of your tablet, e-reader, or laptop. Set your alarm to go into your staff job tomorrow. Don't waste your time. However, if you're like every travel nurse that emphatically answered "YES!" then welcome to the next exciting chapter in your career. My hope is that this book will fully prepare you to enter the wonderful, crazy world of travel nursing that I have called home for almost ten years.

As I'm sure you've gathered from the previous questions, travel nursing is not for every nurse. It requires a specific set of traits to turn a nursing career into a *travel* nursing career. You will need to use every trait that makes you a great nurse, but the most common ones that I've found necessary to make the leap to travel nursing include **fortitude, independence, resourcefulness, confidence, flexibility, and open-mindedness.**

These characteristics are the foundation of the ideal traveler. These traits link arms like Dorothy, the Tin Man, the Scarecrow, and the Cowardly Lion, and skip down the yellow brick road together to every travel assignment. You'll quickly realize how essential they are: you'll be drawing on them from the moment you decide you want to try travel nursing until you finish your last contract, regardless of whether it's a one-contract experiment to rid yourself of debt, or a long-term lifestyle choice like mine. Therefore, it's worth assessing whether you possess these qualities already, or whether you might need to work on them.

According to Merriam-Webster, **fortitude** is "strength of mind that enables a person to encounter danger or bear pain or adversity with courage." Most nurses refer to it as backbone, determination, or guts. Regardless of what you call it, you must have it in abundance. It takes a backbone of steel to leave the safety of familiarity—your family, friends, home, and work—and move hundreds, or even thousands, of miles away. You will be moving into a new apartment, finding your way in a new place, and starting a new job, mostly on your own. To brave such a situation, you will have to call upon every ounce of courage you possess. You might not be on your own for every assignment. But, if you plan to travel for any amount of time, you will eventually run into this situation, especially if you are on your own (which represents the majority of travelers). However, some nurses travel with their spouses, fiancés/fiancées, girl/boyfriends, family members, or even pets. That kind of support can be helpful, but it doesn't alleviate all the stress of starting a new travel assignment.

Independence is another essential trait for travel nursing, especially if you take an assignment far from home. Anyone considering this leap into the unknown would benefit from the experience of living alone, or at least being self-sufficient. If you still take your laundry to your mom, depend on your dad to change your oil, or rely heavily on a handful of friends to keep you entertained on weekends, then travel nursing will be a big ass wake-up call for you. Travel nursing can be overwhelming, even if you have been "on your own" for some time. However, this doesn't necessarily mean you will hate traveling if you're not used to being away from loved ones. You just need to be aware that there are times when you need to be comfortable being in your own company. Modern technology enables us to text, call, or video conference with family and friends anywhere, but this is no substitute for good, old-fashioned human contact. I tend to make friends easily, which helps me feel at home wherever I am, but I also don't mind going out and doing things independently. Unless you are traveling with a friend, significant other, or even a pet, you will have periods of alone time when traveling, and this can cause a feeling of loneliness or homesickness. Since this can be such a big issue for some travelers, I will revisit this topic later, in Chapter 12, and offer some solutions.

Resourcefulness is another essential trait needed to thrive in the world of travel nursing. It is the ability to skillfully deal with new situations, difficulties, or just whatever the hell life throws at you. Knowing you possess a substantial amount of resourcefulness, which can be innate or learned, will give you more confidence and a greater willingness to set out on life's journeys with less fear and anxiety. Some would say resourcefulness is the same as "street smarts," but "street smarts" comes from real-life experience. In contrast, resourcefulness can also be learned from others' experiences, books, movies, etc. Whatever the situation, the more resourceful you are, the easier it will be to deal with any problems you encounter.

If you are planning on being a traveler, you will need both personal and professional **confidence**. Possessing fortitude, independence, and resourcefulness will automatically afford you some level of personal confidence, allowing you to trust your ability to take care of yourself and live in an area away from readily available help. Professionally, you need to trust your ability to take care of your assigned patients with little or no assistance. As nurses, we know no one does it alone; but, if a hospital is utilizing travel nurses, their staffing will be less than optimal in some respect. If you can hold your own, you can be a nurse in any environment. As a travel nurse, you are expected to hit the floor running with minimal orientation and guidance in your chosen specialty's patient care basics. Therefore, later in the book, I will discuss the experience requirement for starting travel nursing and why it is more than just having a certain number of years of experience under your belt.

Now we come to flexibility. **Flexibility, adaptability, assimilation**, and **open-mindedness** are all slightly different traits, but they all represent elements of a certain attitude that is invaluable. If you're flexible, you're willing to change to meet people halfway. If you're adaptable, you are readily able to adjust yourself to different conditions. Assimilation is the ability to take in and make as one's own or conform. To be flexible and adaptable, or to assimilate, you must be receptive to new ideas, opinions, or ways of doing things—open-mindedness. You might hear this attitude referred to as "going with the flow." As a travel nurse, it's essential because there is a possibility you could start at a new hospital and move to a new place every 13 weeks. This is generally not the case because contract extensions are common if the hospital continues to need travel nurses and you like the facility and your colleagues. For example, I spent nine months in San Antonio, TX, and a year each in Little Rock, AR, and Louisville, KY. But the point stands: you need to be ready to pack up and move regularly, which requires that you're open to change.

Wherever you find yourself, and however frequently you change location, you will have to adapt to your new surroundings. On a personal level, you will need to familiarize yourself with your new home. You will need to find the grocery store, general-purpose store, the post office, maybe a place to tan or work out, and, finally, where you will be working. Other sites handy to look up might be restaurants, an automotive shop (for oil changes or if you have problems with your vehicle), the local movie theater, and any other points of interest.

While you are adapting on a personal level, you will also be adjusting professionally to your new work environment. This usually starts with hospital and unit orientation. Most hospitals require travelers to go through the same orientation as staff, albeit abbreviated, requiring that you learn quickly. Hospital orientation is an excellent place to start to understand how things run at any facility. Some hospitals are extremely streamlined and run at maximum efficiency, but most don't. What this means for you, as a traveler, is that, ultimately, you must adapt to the way your new hospital does things, even if your practice is more efficient and safer. This does not mean that you should ever do anything that you know to be unsafe; it just means you might have to do something less efficiently. As a traveler, you will see many ways of completing the same task and, hopefully, you will adopt the most practical. You can always bring more effective nursing practices with you on assignment;

just don't try to convert the staff. And <u>NEVER</u> say, "But this is the way we did it at XYZ Hospital." You are there to fill a gap in staffing, not change the system. If that is your plan, I suggest switching from bedside nursing to hospital/nursing administration. The best advice is to practice safely, follow the specific hospital's protocols, and do the job you were hired to do.

How to Use This Book

This book is for nurses and nursing students considering travel nursing in their career. It will guide you through the process of getting into travel nursing in the US and its territories for US-based nurses. **Chapter 1** offers a look into the history of travel nursing and the types of contingent staffing utilized to meet hospitals' needs. **Chapter 2** covers the items necessary to start with travel healthcare agencies, with tips and tricks for getting them together and organized. It also looks thoroughly at the experience needed to dive in. **Chapter 3** covers the all-important topic of money and how it flows in the travel nursing industry. In **Chapter 4**, I will guide you through the jungle of travel healthcare agencies and how to find the best fit for you. **Chapter 5** is all about finding and applying for travel jobs, and how to break down the pay packages so you can compare "apples to apples." **Chapter 6** guides you through the interviewing process with prospective hospitals and how to navigate their computerized interviewing systems. **Chapter 7** is all about how to deal with contracts and resigning from your staff job without burning any bridges. In **Chapter 8**, I'll guide you through the many housing options that exist for travel nurses, how to evaluate them, and how to deal with it when they don't work for you. **Chapters 9 and 10** cover everything about preparing you and your belongings for the journey to your assignment location. **Chapter 11** is all about moving into your temporary housing and becoming comfortable in your new surroundings. It also covers how to make great first impressions at your assignment and what you can possibly expect from your new co-workers. **Chapter 12** covers the tips and tricks on enjoying your assignment location with, or without, friends and acquaintances. **Chapter 13** covers the steps to repeat if you have found travel nursing is your niche, considerations when planning to take time off, and the "Big Checklist" of the steps to take from beginning to end. Lastly, the **Resources Section** is loaded with websites, lists, extra tips, and information about every topic covered in this book to give you the best chances for a wonderful travel nursing experience.

As you continue reading, I will expose you to, and prepare you for, the ways of getting started in the travel nursing world, so you can enjoy the experience and not feel the need to throw a pail of water, or drop a house on a witch or two, along your journey down the yellow brick road. Remember, "You're not in Kansas anymore!" You've entered the wild, wonderful travel nursing land of Oz.

CHAPTER 1

——

What is a
Travel Nurse?

To move, to breathe, to fly, to float,
To gain all while you give,
To roam the roads of lands remote,
To travel is to live.

HANS CHRISTIAN ANDERSEN

SINCE YOU'RE READING THIS BOOK, IT IS OBVIOUS you have been exposed to travel nursing in some form. You have seen an ad in a nursing journal or magazine, your best friend's cousin's girlfriend is a travel nurse, or you've worked with one on your unit. You probably have some idea that a travel nurse goes from hospital to hospital around the country and gets paid to do so. You may have visions of a nurse sitting on the beach, laying in a hammock, or hiking through jungle-like terrain. All these visions are real, but there is more to the story, *much more*. This chapter will cover a brief history of travel nursing, the most common myths around travel nursing, and the four types of contingent staffing.

When Did Travel Nursing Begin?

Travel nursing began with Florence Nightingale in October 1854, when she and 38 nurses traveled to the Ottoman Empire to assist with their injured soldiers' care in their war with the Russian Empire. This is the first example of travel nurses meeting needs in a crisis, but there weren't any contracts, reimbursements, or stipends involved, unlike modern travel nursing. Today's travel nursing began on October 30, 1978, in my homeland of Louisiana at Tulane University Medical Center in New Orleans, when seven Boston-based nurses from the Traveling Nurse Corps started the first-ever travel nursing assignments. Throughout 1979, the travelers helped Tulane with the increased workload related to staff vacations and census spike of the Mardi Gras season that February. Mardi Gras is always a big, crazy party with hundreds of thousands of visitors partying like the south Louisiana natives that have been conditioned since birth for the weeks-long celebration. It was extra crazy in '79, with the New Orleans Police out on strike and the National Guard filling in, with a mission to only protect against persons and property crimes. As a result, ERs saw an even greater than average increase in the patient census that year, with wilder than usual Mardi Gras partying. As the national nursing shortage grew in the 1980s, other facilities across the country took note of the use of outside help, and the travel nursing industry exploded. The basic idea of travel nursing is to fill the nursing needs in areas experiencing shortages: either because of a lack of nurses for the average patient census, or for patient census increases related to an influx of population, flu season, and epidemics/pandemics like Ebola in 2014, SARS in 2009, and, most recently, COVID-19.

Myths and Facts about Travel Nursing

Myth: Travel nursing is only for the young and free.

Truth: Travel nurses cover all age groups, marital statuses, and the number and age of dependents. The two largest groups of travelers are the young, free ones and the empty nesters, but there are also some in the middle. I worked with a nurse in California whose husband worked remotely. They traveled with their two young children and worked together on homeschooling them. It must have been working for them because she was in her fifth year of travel with the husband and kids. Another nurse I worked with in Oklahoma had retired from her staff position of 25 years, and she and her husband used her taking travel contracts to "vacation" in their retirement. Another nurse traveled with her elderly father and her young son. This is the proof you can do it, regardless of age, marital status, family obligations, etc. It just requires planning.

Myth: You must travel to a different assignment every 13 weeks.

Truth: A typical travel assignment is 13 weeks in length, but I can attest that you do not have to travel to a different assignment *every* 13 weeks. Most assignments offer contract extensions. In fact, I have only had one assignment in ten years where an extension was not offered. In that instance, I knew there wouldn't be because I was filling in for a nurse on maternity leave. However, as I've stated in the preface, I have spent up to a year in one place with several contracts.

Myth: Travel nursing does not provide a steady source of income, or travel nursing is a less stable career choice.

Truth: I am calling BS on this one. I have been consistently employed for years, only being without a contract when I *wanted* to be.

I have been employed year-round for the last five years. As a travel nurse, I have had greater control over my career, time off, vacations, etc., than when I was a staff nurse. As a staff nurse, I had neither the time nor money for vacations because I only earned so much paid time off per pay period. Now, every day I don't have to work is a vacation, because I am a tourist where I'm temporarily living for work. If you want to be employed year-round as a traveler, you will need to find an agency with numerous assignment options year-round, which I will cover in Chapter 4: Researching and Choosing an Agency.

Myth: I can't work as a travel nurse close to my home.

Truth: Some contracts do have a mile radius restriction, preventing healthcare professionals from applying for assignments in their local area, but not all. I have worked contracts all along the Interstate 10/12 corridor from New Orleans to Lake Charles, which kept me within three hours of home. I'm currently working with a travel nurse in Little Rock who works her required shifts in a row, then returns to her home two and a half hours from the hospital. I also worked with a local contract nurse who lived just outside Louisville, KY. This brings me to contingent staffing types that could give you the travel career that works for you.

The Four Types of Contingent Staffing

The basic definition of a contingent staffing nurse is one filling a gap in staffing needs for hospitals and facilities. The needs may be related to a lack of experienced nurses, a leave of absence, or seasonal population fluctuations. There are four types of contingent staffing help: PRN, local, travel, and seasonal. PRN is also known as per diem, or "by the day." These nurses can be staff nurses of the specific hospital, or work for an agency that offers nurses on a day-by-day basis for staffing needs such as call-ins, overnight spikes in the patient census, or to cover for a nurse taking a day off from a small business, like a clinic or outpatient surgical center which has limited access to surplus nurses. These nurses are not full-time employees, are not guaranteed hours, and are generally not entitled to benefits. PRN is the type of position many travelers maintain at their home facilities during their first few contracts if travel nursing isn't their calling.

Local and travel nurses make up the largest portion of contingent staffing nurses and are different from PRN. First, local and travel nurses have contracts that can guarantee a specific number of weeks and hours per week. The hours per week are generally 36 to 48, depending on the number of hours per day (8, 10, 12) and number of days per week (3, 4, 5). The contracts can range from 4 to 26 weeks, with 13 weeks being the norm. These contracts are based on hospitals' perceived needs and are handled through a healthcare staffing agency. These nurses become part of the hospitals' scheduling processes and will have their work dates 4, 6, or 8 weeks at a time. The differences between local and travel contracts are twofold. First, a travel contract has a rule, generally set by the facility, that the nurse must reside a certain number of miles or more away from the facility, generally 50, 75, or 100, while local contracts do not. The second difference is the pay. With local contracts, it is assumed you are not duplicating your living expenses, since you are expected to be living at home as a local; thus, the pay package is structured differently—no housing stipends (I will get into travel pay packages in Chapter 3).

Lastly, seasonal contracts are perhaps the most unique form of contingent staffing. These contracts are prevalent in regions where snowbirds flock in the winter to escape the cold, such as Arizona, California, and Florida, and are open to any nurse not employed by the facility. They differ from travel contracts in that they are typically offered directly through the hiring hospital, without an agency's help. However, you may find an agency with a seasonal contract from time to time. They often last for six months, from the fall to early spring, and usually offer higher hourly rates than the hospital would otherwise pay, as well as sign-on and completion bonuses. However, they often only offer a trimmed benefits package, or no benefits at all.

Many travelers combine all the contingent staffing types into their travel nursing career. I've worked with nurses who travel to Arizona every winter as a seasonal nurse for six months, then return home for local contracts for the other six and repeat this yearly. Others, like me, do travel contracts year-round. I have also worked with nurse educators who do a single 13-week travel contract per year during a semester when they are not teaching. My focus for this book is travel nursing, but I wanted you to be aware of the options to create the travel nursing life you want. To create that life, you must get started with a nursing travel agency. In the next three chapters, I will go over the items you'll need for the agencies, how the pay works, and how to choose an agency.

CHAPTER 2

Getting Organized: Preparing the Required Documents

For every minute spent organizing, an hour is earned.
Benjamin Franklin

CONGRATULATIONS!! If you have made it this far, you've obviously got the travel bug, have the necessary personality traits, a basic understanding of the types of contingent staffing and contracts, and a grasp of what to expect as a traveler living a life on the road. You are ready to begin pulling together the less exciting but necessary paperwork: your "passport" for travel nursing. While this is the tedious part of travel nursing, organizing your documents will truly make credentialing a breeze from contract-to-contract and agency-to-agency, allowing you to get started quicker. As I guide you through this chapter, I want you to think of all the position requirements, documents, and tests, required of you by your staff facility as you were getting started, because those items will be required again by the agencies. With that in mind, let's dive in!

Basic Requirements

The basic requirements are the same as any bedside nurse position you find listed on a hospital's HR website and are mostly self-explanatory. You will need to:

- be a graduate of an accredited nursing program
- pass the NCLEX
- possess an unencumbered nursing license
- be legally eligible to work in the US
- pass a physical stating you can function as a nurse
- pass a urine drug screen
- provide documentation of vaccinations, certifications, and BLS/ACLS/PALS (depending on specialty)
- provide two or more references from (a) recent nursing position(s)
- provide an updated résumé
- possess **experience**

Let's explore some of these in more detail below.

Nursing Licenses

To become active with a nursing travel agency, which can also be referred to as a travel healthcare agency, you just need to possess a nursing license; but to travel, you must possess a compact (multistate) nursing license, or multiple single state licenses for the locations you are going to work in. If you are fortunate enough to live in one of the 34 compact states, it is going to make the journey a hell of a lot easier. However, if you are like me and reside in a non-compact state, don't despair. It is possible to enjoy a travel career; you are just going to have to put in a little more legwork by collecting nursing licenses for the states you want to work in. At one point in my travel career, I believe I held up to 12 active state licenses, and you know that ain't cheap. So, I am grateful that Louisiana finally went compact in 2019, and I now only need to get licenses for non-compact states. To learn which states are compact and which are not, visit the National Council of State Boards of Nursing website. Before moving to the next requirement, a little discussion is needed about compact and non-compact licenses, and preparation for getting multiple licenses for non-compact license holders. Please understand you do not need to get a bunch of licenses before starting with an agency. If you wait until you are working for an agency, you will be reimbursed for the licensing process when it pertains to a specific contract you accept.

Compact States

If you live in a compact state, congratulations! You won't need to spend lots of time and money acquiring new state licenses. However, the first thing you need to do is make sure you hold a multistate license. If your state recently went compact, they might not automatically convert your single-state license to multistate. In this case, you must apply for it. Even if your state has been compact for a while, you may not hold a multistate license because of reasons of exclusion, such as previous license probation or suspension, felony charges, or participation in an alternative program. Check your state's board of nursing website to find requirements for conversion to a multistate license and reasons for exclusion.

Non-compact States

My non-compact state brethren, it's time to prepare yourself for becoming well acquainted with applying for nursing licenses. I will share with you a few plan-ahead tips I've learned from apply-ing for the many nursing licenses I once held. While many states have moved their applications online, there will still be physical paperwork involved. First, you should find out the process for re-questing official transcripts from your <u>initial</u> RN (ADN or BSN) program school. You will need that for each state you apply to for license endorsement. However, don't request a pile to keep and send later as you apply for other states. The states generally want them to be sent directly from the school or a third-party vendor (i.e. Parchment or National Student Clearinghouse) to help main-tain the validity of the documents.

Licensure Verification

Next, learn the license verification process for your current state. At the time of this publication, all states use the Nursys® li-censure verification system, which makes life so easy, but there are times when a state's verification information data is not linked to Nursys®. In these instances, the verification process is available on the nursing board's website and you will need it for every license endorsement application. Whether using the Nursys® system or the state board's process, keep the receipt for the cost of verifica-tion because you must have proof of expense for reimbursement from the agency. Another item frequently requested for the appli-cation is a 2" x 2" passport-style photo of the applicant. This is easy enough to deal with, as most Walgreens or CVS photo centers offer passport photo services. I recommend getting two sets and scan-ning one of the photos to your cloud storage system, as you never know when you will need an ID-style photo.

Fingerprinting

Next, think about the states you might want to travel to, go to their board of nursing websites, and request fingerprint cards to be sent to you. If you live in a state offering digital fingerprinting services, they may be able to send your prints electronically. However, not every state accepts digital prints, hence the fingerprint cards. If the location can send the prints electronically, you will need to wait until after you apply for the license, because they will need the application tracking number to link your prints to the application. All digital fingerprinting places should offer traditional fingerprinting too because they can print your scanned prints onto the cards. In the Resources section are websites of digital fingerprinting companies which offer the option of making appointments, which I highly recommend. But, if none of them are near your location, your fingerprints can be done at local and state police offices. Getting several fingerprint cards completed at once will help speed up the process when you start applying for RN endorsements. Note: do not send the cards to the respective board of nursing until you complete the application and pay the associated fees, because upon completion you will receive an ID specific to you and your application for fingerprint card association.

Lastly, if you have a past that involved rides in the backs of cop cars, or an overnight stay in a jail cell, be prepared to write up a statement of the situation, the judgment, and outcome for each incident. I would also find out how to get official documents related to the situation, because most state boards will require the full rundown before they decide whether to issue a license endorsement for their state.

Proof of Eligibility to Work in the US

Any agency will require proof that you have the authority to work in the US in the form of identification documents listed on the USCIS I-9 form. For you, that means you need a current US passport, permanent resident card, or an alien registration receipt; or a driver's license and US Social Security card or US birth certificate. For the full, updated list of acceptable documents, visit the US Citizenship and Immigration Services website. I have included the most current I-9 form (at the time of publication) in the Resources section, as well as the web address.

Documentation

The travel agency will also require copies of your RN license or proof through Nursys® and BLS/ACLS/PALS, as appropriate to the specialty you will be traveling in, as well as immunization records, titer results, fit tests, and any specialty certifications. For a detailed list, visit the Resources section. I <u>strongly</u> recommend that, as you are getting these items together, you:

1. Make sure they don't expire for at least six months with regards to BLS/ACLS/PALS. If they do, get them renewed, even if you have four or five months left before expiration.

2. Make electronic copies and save them to whatever cloud storage system you use, so they are easily accessible when needed. As a rule of thumb, make electronic copies of all documents—renewals, re-certs, immunizations, and fit tests—to prevent you from having to repeat them unnecessarily.

References

While you are collecting all those documents for your travel nurse "passport," you will also want to collect the contact information (i.e. phone number and email) for five or six superiors that can attest to your nursing skills—nurse managers, nurse supervisors, charge nurses, or preceptors. I'm suggesting five or six because, in Chapter 4, I will guide you towards working with three different travel companies, each of which requires at least two references. Yes, you could use the same two references for all three companies but, as an educator, I have served as a reference for new grads getting their first jobs and I know what it's like to repeat yourself several times to different companies. Be kind and spread out these requests for references among your contacts.

Your Résumé

The last plan-ahead tip I have is to update your résumé so it's ready to roll (example in the Resources section). Your résumé will be the foundation of the profile that is submitted by the agency to prospective hospitals in order to apply for a travel contract. Some agencies allow you to upload your résumé document to their website as you apply, others have an application asking for résumé-related information. Either way, getting it all together beforehand speeds up the process later. As you prepare and update your résumé, focus on these critical pieces of information about the jobs you've held: hospital size, including number of beds overall and on the unit; whether it's teaching or non-teaching; trauma level; type of unit (specialty); the nurse-to-patient ratio; the electronic charting system used; and any specialty equipment on the unit that you're trained to use. Other items to include are RN license(s), including whether they are single state or compact and their expiration dates, and specialty certifications and their respective expiration dates. I have created an example that is listed in the Resources section. You want to make yourself as marketable as possible. If you are eligible, get a certification in the specialty you want to travel in. You don't need it to travel, but it will lead to more offers because certifications prove that you hold special knowledge beyond the basics. This lets the profile reviewer at the prospective hospital know you have more than what they are looking for to fill the gap, and it will help you to stand out.

How Much Experience Do I Need?

The most frequent question I get from anyone considering travel is, "How much nursing experience do I need to start traveling?" If you have done any research into becoming a travel nurse, you've probably seen answers to this question ranging from one to two years, depending on which agency website you view. I want you to know that this stipulation is based on the experience requirements of the travel contracts represented by the agency. If the agency mostly represents contracts requiring one year of experience, they will require one year of experience to start with them.

My response to this question regarding experience is often, "Enough that you feel comfortable doing your job anywhere and in any situation." This is not to say that you need to be a walking textbook of all things nursing, but you must at least have a comfort level with your practice. I have made this my answer because of years of travel with both "good" and "bad" contracts. The good ones need my help to fill a small gap because of staff on maternity leave or family medical leave. They had enough nurses and ancillary staff to provide the necessary care to the patients without stretching staff too thin. For me, as a travel nurse, this meant I had the help I needed and enough staff to answer my questions. As I'm sure you've concluded already, the bad contracts were mostly the opposite. They were at facilities that didn't have enough nurses (staff or travel); the nurse-to-patient ratios were on the edge of dangerous for the patients and my license; and there was little, to no, support from the facility. I'm grateful the bad contracts have been few and far between, but they exist, so I want you to be prepared.

We all progress at different rates and learn differently, thus my answer above is not time specific. I will say that I *highly* recommend two years of nursing before traveling if you are fresh out of school. We have all heard the saying, "You learn more in your first year of nursing than you did in all of nursing school," which is absolutely true. Therefore, two years will give you time to learn the things you can't learn in nursing school, hone your assessment and time management skills, learn proper delegation, and make you a more seasoned nurse that can stand on your own two feet. If you have been practicing for years, you should be good to go; just keep in mind that not all units in a specialty are created the same. Again, I remind you that two years is a suggestion, and I passionately believe in the guiding principle of, "Enough experience that you feel comfortable doing your job anywhere and in any situation." I want you to be experienced enough that you can deal with anything: whether your patient is circling the drain or flying high; whether there are no nursing assistants, or so many you're tripping over them; or if the shit is hitting the fan in every room and no one *can* help because everyone *needs* help.

Another important point to be made is that it's not a good idea to switch specialties while being a travel nurse. This is something to be done as a staff nurse, as you will receive the required orientation and guidance that you will almost never receive as a traveler, when you are expected to hit the ground running in a most likely understaffed unit. I went from telemetry to CVICU by returning to a staff position because I knew I'd need the focused support and stability of a team to train me to an appropriate level. If a facility is in a tight enough jam, they are willing to train a travel nurse with a similar skill set to the area they are applying for, but I wouldn't count on that training giving you adequate preparation for an assignment in the specialty at another facility.

Facilities have experience requirements in their contracts because they expect you to hit the ground running, with little to no orientation to the hospital or the unit. Some travel nurse agencies may try to tempt you to work for them with less experience, in order for them to make more money. Please don't...it's your nursing license on the line and this should be a red flag as to their standards of professionalism. On a personal note, I did not begin as a travel nurse until I had been practicing for three years. The three years was split between orthopedics, neurology, and telemetry, and, looking back there was still a significant learning curve when I started traveling in the med-surg/telemetry specialty.

Now you know all the essential items required to begin building your profile with a travel healthcare agency. We've covered the difference between compact and non-compact licenses, how to have your license verified, and fingerprinting for licensure endorsements. In the Resources section, you can find a concise list of the items covered in this chapter to help you get organized and ready for starting with an agency, which will be covered in Chapter 4. But first, I will cover money in the travel world— pay packages, taxable, non-taxable, subsidies, and reimbursements.

CHAPTER 3

Show Me the Money! Understanding Pay Packages

An investment in knowledge pays the best interest.
BENJAMIN FRANKLIN

YOU'RE PROBABLY WONDERING WHY THERE IS A discussion about money before I've even told you how to get into an agency to make money. Bottom-line: I want you to be well-informed about how the money in the industry flows, so you don't fall for the wooing tactics I've seen used by many of the agencies to get new-to-travel nurses on board, such as "free" housing, "paid" credentialing costs, and travel and licensing "reimbursements." The one and only rule regarding travel money is… NOTHING is free.

First, let's look at the differences between how staff nurses and travel nurses are paid. As a full-time staff nurse of a facility, you receive a paycheck every week or two. The check is based on wages from the hours you work minus income taxes, social security taxes, insurance premiums, and retirement account contributions.

Travel nurses receive pay packages that include wages from hours worked, housing subsidy, travel reimbursement, meals and incidentals subsidy, and licensure/certification reimbursements. They still pay the same taxes as permanent staff, but not *all* the money travelers get is taxed. Now, let's get down to the nitty gritty of how travel nurses' pay packages are created.

How Are Travel Nurse Pay Packages Created?

Every dollar starts with the bill rate, which is the amount a hospital is willing to pay per hour the travel nurse works. If your agency used an MSP (Managed Service Provider) or VMS (Vendor Management System) for the contract, three to six percent is taken right off the top to pay for access to the contract. If it is a direct or exclusive contract, then the middleman is cut out leaving more money in the pay package. Then your agency will take 15 to 25 percent from what is left to pay your recruiter, agency expenses, and agency profit. You get everything that is left. For example, a $100 bill rate will leave you approximately $75 per hour. This will be broken down into a taxable hourly rate, nontaxable housing and incidentals stipends, nontaxable reimbursements, insurance, and those pesky income taxes we all pay.

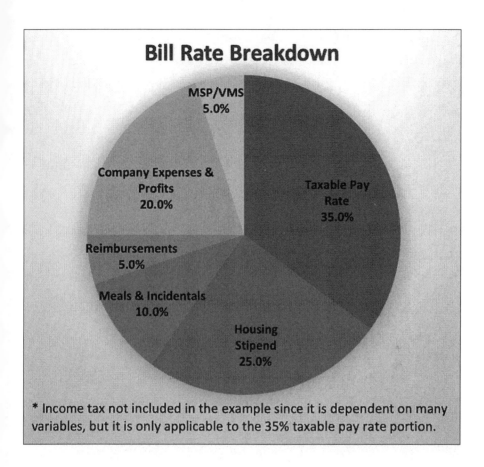

Bill Rate Breakdown

- MSP/VMS 5.0%
- Company Expenses & Profits 20.0%
- Taxable Pay Rate 35.0%
- Reimbursements 5.0%
- Meals & Incidentals 10.0%
- Housing Stipend 25.0%

* Income tax not included in the example since it is dependent on many variables, but it is only applicable to the 35% taxable pay rate portion.

What is a MSP/VMS?

An MSP and a VMS are, for the purposes of this book, central repositories of travel nurse contracts. These allow agencies, especially smaller ones, access to hundreds of contracts that they would otherwise not have access to. This is not to say that larger agencies don't utilize MSP/VMS; they are just more frequently used by smaller agencies because of their lack of exclusive or direct contracts. Hence, you will notice the same contracts being presented through multiple agencies. If the thought popped into your head that you will just avoid companies that use MSPs or VMSs so you can have more money available to you, based on the example above, just keep reading.

Travel Agency Fees

Yes, any travel agency out there will make money from your work. They need to pay their overheads and make a profit, like any business. The hospital where you work does the same thing, but just in a different fashion. Below is a list of agency costs funded by the money it makes from your contract. The items marked with an asterisk (*) are benefits for you.

Office staff	Exhibitor fee at recruiting events
Recruiter salaries	Liability insurance
Rents	* Licensing/credentialing
Utilities	Agency profits
Business insurance	* Guaranteed hours
* Employee benefits	Contract cancellations
Advertising	* Non-billable orientation hours
Office supplies	* Referral bonuses

Travel agencies vary in size and desired profit margins, hence the ten percent variance in what they might take from your pay. The larger the agency, the greater the overhead, thus the more money kept from the bill rate. However, this doesn't necessarily mean you should only use smaller companies. The larger companies generally have more contracts and location options compared to the smaller ones. Also, smaller companies generally don't have exclusive contracts with specific hospital systems, so almost all their contracts go through an MSP/VMS, meaning you will lose an extra three to six percent over the company fees/profits. Thus, you must decide what is important to you: making more money with a small agency (with a fee of 23 percent to 26 percent), but not getting to be in a particular locale; or getting a specific, desired location with the larger agency, but losing up to 30 percent.

Taxable Pay Rate

This part of the pay package is liable for income taxes and is probably the least important thing to consider for a travel nurse. "Why isn't this the most important part?" you're probably asking yourself. Well, the basic rule…less income = less taxes. Thus, many agencies offer minor rates for hours worked for most of the contracts, leaving most of your income untouched by taxes in the form of housing subsidy and reimbursements. To make you aware, some hospitals set a minimum hourly taxable rate as part of their contract with the agency, MSP, or VMS, which will limit the amount of untaxed money available to you. This is explained in the next section.

Untaxed Money (The Best Money!)

The untaxed portion of your pay package is the meat and potatoes of a traveler's pay and can really increase the overall net amount you receive. In the early years of the industry, some agencies offered so much of the pay package within the untaxed portion that travelers were making just above minimum wage in their taxed hourly rate. This caused the IRS to take notice and they began cracking down on the agencies doing this, with fines and penalties. Subsequently, even the travelers that worked for the agencies were targeted because they were not paying appropriate taxes. Thankfully, the agencies practicing illegal financials have been shut down or gone out of business, meaning one less thing you have to worry about. But I am going to show you how to make sure that everything related to tax-free money in your contract is above board and won't land you in hot water with the IRS.

I would like to introduce you to your new friend: the US General Services Administration (GSA) website's travel section. This website summarizes the allowance limits set by the IRS for housing, meals and incidentals, and mileage for each fiscal year based on the location of the contract facility. The website will ask for a city and state because each location has a different limit based on costs in the area and time of the year. For example, for a contract in San Francisco, CA, the agency would be allowed to give you a **maximum** per day of $302 for housing and $76 for meals and incidentals for a contract that goes from January 1 to March 31, 2020, as well as 57.5¢ per mile to drive your vehicle to and from the contract city. If you worked in San Francisco from October 1 to December 31, 2019, the maximum per day would have been $334 for housing in October and $244 in November and December, with meals, incidentals, and travel staying the same. This does not mean you will get the maximum amount for housing, meals and incidentals, and travel reimbursement in your pay package, as hospitals will set the contract amounts based on their own budgets, but that is what you can *legally* have.

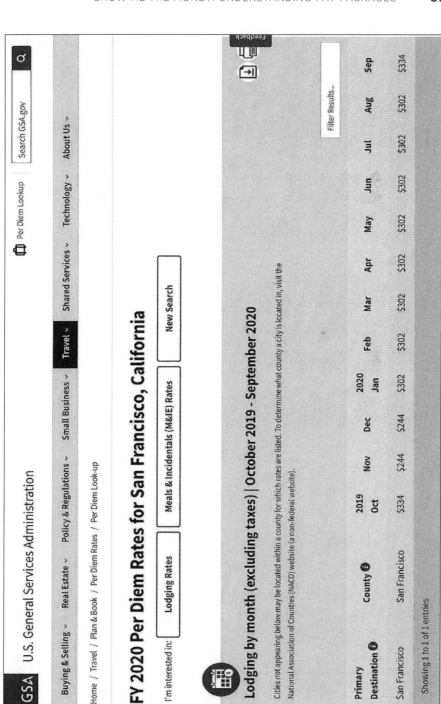

GSA   U.S. General Services Administration

Per Diem Lookup | Search GSA.gov

Buying & Selling ⌄   Real Estate ⌄   Policy & Regulations ⌄   Small Business ⌄   Travel ⌄   Shared Services ⌄   Technology ⌄   About Us ⌄

Home / Travel / Plan & Book / Per Diem Rates / Per Diem Look-up

Meals & Incidentals (M&IE) Breakdown ⓘ

Use this table to find the following information for federal employee travel:

M&IE Total - the full daily amount received for a single calendar day of travel when that day is neither the first nor last day of travel.

Breakfast, lunch, dinner, incidentals - Separate amounts for meals and incidentals. M&IE Total = Breakfast + Lunch + Dinner + Incidentals. Sometimes meal amounts must be deducted from trip voucher. See More Information

First & last day of travel - amount received on the first and last day of travel and equals 75% of total M&IE.

Filter Results...

Primary Destination ⓘ	County ⓘ	M&IE Total	Continental Breakfast/Breakfast	Lunch	Dinner	Incidental Expenses	First & Last Day of Travel ⓘ
San Francisco	San Francisco	$76	$18	$19	$34	$5	$57.00

Showing 1 to 1 of 1 entries

Feedback

In a smaller location like Tyler, TX, for example, you would be allowed to have $96 per day for housing, without regard to the months of the contract during the fiscal year of 2020. This area does not experience a "high-demand" season, like major metropolitan areas, thus no change in housing pay like the San Francisco example. Meal and incidentals allowance for the Tyler area would garner $55 per day. The mileage reimbursement is 57.5¢, like San Francisco, because this number is set each tax year and applies to all private vehicle travel for work purposes.

Thus, you can see how this can change, or not, from month-to-month, year-to-year, and location-to-location, and why the GSA website is your friend. Lastly, reimbursements for licenses and certifications renewals, uniforms, and continuing education are untaxed and can be built into your pay package based on the remaining available funds from the bill rate.

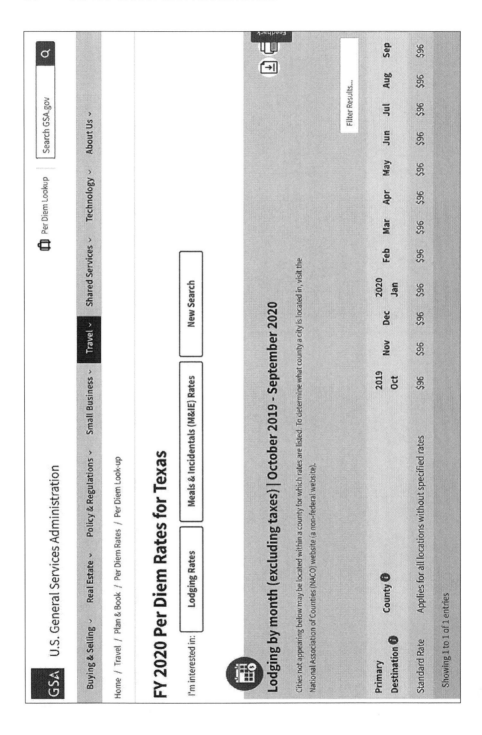

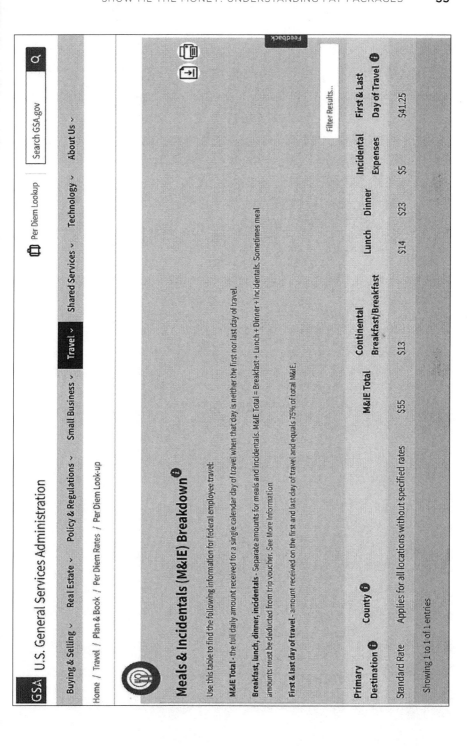

GSA U.S. General Services Administration

Per Diem Lookup   Search GSA.gov

Buying & Selling ∨   Real Estate ∨   Policy & Regulations ∨   Small Business ∨   Travel ∨   Shared Services ∨   Technology ∨   About Us ∨

Home / Travel / Plan & Book / Per Diem Rates / Per Diem Look-up

Meals & Incidentals (M&IE) Breakdown ⓘ

Use this table to find the following information for federal employee travel:

M&IE Total - the full daily amount received for a single calendar day of travel when that day is neither the first nor last day of travel.

Breakfast, lunch, dinner, incidentals - Separate amounts for meals and incidentals. M&IE Total = Breakfast + Lunch + Dinner + Incidentals. Sometimes meal amounts must be deducted from trip voucher. See More Information

First & last day of travel - amount received on the first and last day of travel and equals 75% of total M&IE.

Filter Results...

Primary Destination ⓘ	County ⓘ	M&IE Total	Continental Breakfast/Breakfast	Lunch	Dinner	Incidental Expenses	First & Last Day of Travel ⓘ
Standard Rate	Applies for all locations without specified rates	$55	$13	$14	$23	$5	$41.25

Showing 1 to 1 of 1 entries

Feedback

Overtime Pay Rate

Now, I want to speak to my overtime loving workers. First, you know from your staff position that time-and-a-half is the basic rule for overtime rates. The travel companies know that too, so some will try to take advantage of the newbie, but here's the lowdown to keep that from happening to you. Your overtime rate should be at least the total of what you get per hour for housing, meals and incidentals, and hourly taxable pay rate for your contracted hours per week. Below are two examples of previous contracts that illustrate fair overtime pay:

	Example 1 ($ Per Hour)	Example 2 ($ Per Hour)
Taxable Hourly Rate	20.00	58.35
Taxable OT Hourly Rate	44.00	87.53
Housing Subsidy	15.28	14.70
Meals & Incidentals	6.94	8.36

In Example 1, the overtime rate is more than double the hourly rate, but it is approximately equal per hour to the hourly pay rate, housing, and meals added together (with overtime being a few more dollars, which covers the one-time reimbursements amounts.) In Example 2, the overtime rate is one-and-a-half times the hourly, but it too is the taxable hourly, housing, and meals added together, with the overtime having a few more dollars per hour, again covering reimbursement amounts.

If an agency only offers you one-and-a-half times the taxable hourly rate and it does not equal the taxable hourly, plus the housing and meals (like Example 2), you will be making the agency more money than you make for yourself with any overtime hours. You have two options:

1. You can accept the contract. I do it all the time because I DON'T work overtime. I did enough of that in my 20s to take me through all required 36-hour weeks of my 30s. With this option, I'm not making extra money for the company, but I also limit myself if I want to work an extra shift or two.

2. Don't work for the agency. There are plenty to choose from and, in the next chapter, I will help you find ones that fit you.

Missed Hours or Shifts

Before we leave the topic of money, I want to make you aware of what can happen financially if you have to miss a shift, whether you're sick, need a mental health day, have a family emergency, etc. As I stated at the beginning of the chapter, everything begins with the bill rate, which is what the hospital pays per hour for your work. If you don't work, they don't pay, and you can lose more than just money for the missed shift(s). Your housing subsidy and meals and incidentals reimbursement are based on your contracted hours per week (36, 48). If you miss a 12-hour shift, the agency can withhold 12 hours' worth of housing subsidy and meals and incidental reimbursement. If you find your own housing, you will see a decreased amount in your paycheck under the housing and meal/incidentals section (housing is discussed in Chapter 8). However, if you take agency-provided housing, the agency will deduct the amount from your paycheck to cover the cost of paying for your housing at the beginning of the month with the understanding, per your contract, that you would work to earn your housing (which, in this case, you didn't).

In this chapter, we covered how a pay package is built, what items are taxed and not, how to determine if you are being paid appropriately for overtime hours, how agencies spend the money they make from your contract, and what happens when you don't work your contracted hours. What I haven't covered is what is required for the non-taxed items in the pay package to be free of income taxes. I am not a tax expert, but Joseph Smith, RRT, EA, MS Tax, is. He specializes in taxes for travelers and was a travel healthcare professional himself, once upon a time. He maintains a website and blog full of pertinent tax information for travelers, which is listed in the Resources section.

Right now, it's time to find a few agencies to work for. In the next chapter, I'll go over finding the right agency, with a list of questions to help you interview agencies; what to expect and what you should and shouldn't tolerate from recruiters; and how you should and shouldn't communicate with your recruiter.

CHAPTER 4

Researching and Choosing an Agency

You've got your résumé, experience, references, and pay package knowledge all lined up like ducks in a row, and you're asking yourself, "What now?" Now is the time to find the right companies and recruiters for you, as this will set you up for success from the start and keep you employed year-round if that is your choice. There are hundreds of companies to choose from, varying in size, locations of offered contracts, benefits, and years in the travel business. You just have to decide what you're looking for and do your due diligence when choosing who you want to have represent you. Below, I'll explore how to research and interview agencies, how many to work with, how to establish a healthy relationship with them, and some common red flags to look out for.

Finding the Right Travel Agency and Recruiter

With the number of agencies available, the search process can quickly become overwhelming. Once you do manage to narrow down the list of agencies you would be willing to work with, then comes the next hurdle: picking a recruiter. They generally just get assigned to you by the agency, but this doesn't mean you should just accept the first suggestion. You will be working with this person closely, possibly for years to come, and they will help to shape the path of your travel nursing life. It's important that you "click" and that they understand and respect your needs and goals. For this to happen, you have to be open and honest about what you want or plan for your travel nursing career. This is where the trial and error come in. I went through several recruiters before I even started interviewing with hospitals for my first contract. One recruiter up and quit, then another was trying to get me to start at a hospital before I even had a license to practice in that hospital's state. This was my life in 2011 when I was getting started in the travel healthcare industry: I didn't have a travel nursing friend to offer recommendations on agencies or recruiters; books like this were almost nonexistent; and blogs about travel nursing weren't a thing.

To help narrow down the list of possible agencies to work for, here are multiple suggestions I can make with the benefit of hindsight:

1. Interview friends or acquaintances that are travel nurses or travel healthcare professionals (PT, OT, ST, RT). They will be able to provide you with their personal experience of specific agencies and recruiters versus the marketing propaganda you will get from agency websites and recruiters. However, remember that what they tell you is *their* experience and not always the general experience.

2. Make a list of questions from the list below that are important to you.

3. Search the internet using the search terms "travel nurse agency" and "travel healthcare staffing agency." Caveat: the agencies listed near the top of the results have the biggest advertising budgets, so scroll down the list and the next pages of results, too. Many of the agency websites have large amounts of information that will answer the agency interview questions below and which will help you determine if the agency is worth putting on your "agencies to interview" list. My one recommendation while you are searching— NEVER fill out a form to have the agency call you. They will call you daily or weekly to the point of harassment because, as we discussed in the pay package chapter, they don't make money unless you are working a contract for them. If you decide you want to get more information from a certain agency, find their email address and send them your questions. This way, you get your answers and all they have is your email. If you call them, they will have your number because of that pesky double-edged sword—caller ID.

4. Lastly, visit the Joint Commission website for Healthcare Staffing Services Certification and the National Association of Travel Healthcare Organizations (NATHO) websites to verify if the agencies you are considering adhere to ethical business practices and commit to high standards of providing quality candidates. For you, this means you can worry less about being cheated financially in your contract or being "guilted" into working in a specialty in which you are marginally qualified to work, just so the agency makes money. (The web addresses are in the Resources section and I've included a list of agencies.) FYI: just because an agency doesn't have these certifications, does not mean they are a bad agency.

Most agencies are similar, with only minor differences; but these differences could be a make or break for you, so the suggestions above and the listed questions below will help highlight these. As I mentioned above, it's likely that a major portion of answers can be found on the agencies' websites, so you should do your research carefully before you contact them. This list may not cover everything that you want to know, but it will help you to start thinking of what is important to you and your situation.

Questions to Ask Travel Agencies

1. What states do they have access to (have contracts available in)?

Agencies may say they have access to "all 50 states," but often, in practice, they only have contracts in maybe half. This could mean they only have one contract in a state that is not your specialty. When I ask this question, I drill down to uncover more detail until I'm certain that the specialty and state I want are regularly available.

2. Do they have direct "exclusive" contracts, or do they rely on MSP/VMS for contracts? Which MSP/VMS(s)?

Exclusive contracts mean the agency's travelers have first access to the contract and more money in their pay package. The agency will attempt to fill the contract from within their available travelers. If they are unable to do so, it is "sub-contracted" out through an MSP/VMS.

3. How long have they been around?

4. Will they reverse market for you?

Reverse marketing is when the customer (your recruiter and

agency) seeks out the hospital for a job rather than hospital putting out a contract.

5. Do they individualize pay packages (legally maxing out the travel reimbursement, meals/incidentals, and housing) based on the GSA/IRS regulations? Or are packages set by agency administration without the ability to negotiate/adjust to fit the traveler's needs?

6. Do they provide guaranteed pay or partial pay when a shift is canceled by the contracted facility?

If the facility cancels your shift, are you guaranteed pay for your non-taxable incomes (housing and meals/incidentals)? If you sign a guaranteed hours contract, meaning you are assured of your hourly pay and non-taxables pay, does it begin with the first hour of cancellation or after a certain number of hours of cancellation?

7. How do they pay overtime or extra time?

Refer to the discussion and examples in Chapter 3's section on Overtime Pay Rate.

8. Do they provide PTO/sick pay after so many worked hours?

Some states require PTO/sick pay regardless of the agency's standard practices, so if you take a contract in California, for example, the company is required to provide PTO. Other agencies provide it regardless of the state you take a contract in.

9. Do they provide one-bedroom furnished housing? Or do they provide a housing stipend?

10. Do they set up and pay for physicals, TB skin testing, urine drug screens, N-95 mask fit testing, etc. for the traveler when required by the contracted facility?

11. Do they provide reimbursements for required licensure, uniforms, CEU testing, certifications, etc.?

12. Does the agency have someone available 24/7 for clinical emergencies or safety concerns not being addressed by the facility?

13. Do they provide medical, dental, and/or vision insurance? If so, does it start on day one of the contract, or is there a waiting period? Are there options/levels to the offerings (high deductible w/HSA, PPO, etc.)?

> Some travelers maintain their own health insurance instead of using the agency's, since they work with multiple agencies and do not want to have to change insurances with each agency change.

14. Which companies provide the insurance options, and what is the average cost?

15. Do they have a 401k program? When can you start contributing? When are you vested? Do they match any portion of your contributions?

16. Do they offer free online CEUs?

*Note: Whether an agency does or doesn't provide the options or benefits questioned above, does not equate to their quality as an agency.

Nomadicare

If you don't feel like going through the process of interviewing numerous agencies and recruiters and you choose not to use the recommendations of your friends, you do have another option: Nomadicare. Laura Latimer, a travel occupational therapist and the founder of Nomadicare and The Empowered Travelers Movement, has completed the painstaking, time-consuming task of interviewing recruiters and has compiled a list of those that adhere to high ethical standards. Her brand offers a recruiter matching program that makes it as easy as filling out your contact information (yes, I know I previously said not to do this—but this is the only situation where I condone it), your desired location, your requirements of an agency, your specialty, and number of years of experience. You will then be matched with two or three recruiters that fit your needs. The great part about Nomadicare's recruiter matching program is that, if the recruiters aren't a fit for you, you can just do the match again and you'll be provided with further options. Whether you use Nomadicare or not to find your agency and recruiter, I recommend you visit the website, because there is plenty of useful information to help guide you through the beginning of your travel nursing journey.

Number of Agencies to Work With

Every traveler who has been in the industry for at least five years will probably give you a different answer on the number travel agencies that they have worked with and are currently working with. When I first began, I worked with one agency for two years, because I didn't know that not all agencies had access to all contracts. Then I learned that the pay rate was not the same for all the nurses working at the same hospital because of exclusive contracts, MSP/VMS, and agency fee differences as I discussed in Chapter 3, so I began to branch out.

After almost ten years, I work with three agencies. I mostly work with just one, the same one I started with all those years ago, because of my recruiter...but we'll get to that in a minute. When I say I work with three, I maintain a current profile and relationship with my recruiters (updated résumé, current BLS/ACLS, vaccinations, physical, skills checklist, knowledge exams, and current references). I do this just in case one of the other two agencies has an interesting assignment that my primary agency doesn't have, or a better financial deal on an assignment my primary does have. It means there is no delay in submitting my profile from the secondary agencies.

The common recommendation is three agencies because any more than that and I believe it gets too difficult to maintain your profile and relationship with them (which ensures you can be submitted quickly, if desired). Make sure the agencies have access to different assignments to cover most of the contracts available. (See Question 2 above.) Otherwise, you're working with three agencies for no reason. You can start with one agency, like I did, and add as you go, or get three all at the beginning. Your call, your travel nursing career.

Now, back to my recruiter, who I have been with for almost ten years. Earlier in this chapter, I mentioned "clicking" with your recruiter and how it is important. This is true because a great recruiter can make a crappy agency seem great, but a crappy recruiter can make a phenomenal agency suck. Also, having been with the same recruiter for so long, she knows the way I work and the assignments I will consider. You will build a rapport as long as you're open about what you want and need, which is coming up in the next section.

Establishing Expectations

Whichever agencies you choose to represent you, there are a few things you want to make sure are clear from the beginning of the relationship. I use the term relationship because it is a team effort. The agency represents you by helping you to look as great as possible on paper to prospective hospitals. You work for the agency by taking a contract from which, as we've already discussed, they make money. So, it's reasonable that both sides should have appropriate expectations of each other.

Once you have decided on your agencies, you will most likely be dealing with the initial recruiter from your first interactions (when you were asking the Agency Interview Questions). It is now time to have the expectations discussion, so you and the recruiter have a clear understanding of what you both need from each other to make it a successful relationship.

The expectations discussion should include items such as:

1. You expect to work with more than one agency and the recruiter should not make you feel guilty about it; you in return should not/will not pit recruiters/agencies against one another (more on this in Chapter 5).

2. The timeliness of responses to communication by both parties, with realistic expectations based on each party's work schedule.

3. The recruiter will let you know when they have a planned absence, with information on who will be covering for them should you need assistance.

4. Your goals for your travel nursing career (money, location, etc.) so the recruiter knows which kind of assignments to tell you about ASAP.

5. The recruiter should always give you the full pay package (hourly rate, OT rate, housing stipend, meals and incidentals

reimbursement, and travel reimbursement) before submitting you.

6. The recruiter should always offer the most money they can based on the bill rate and set agency fees and profits.

7. You will let the recruiter know what positions other agencies have submitted you for to prevent double submissions. The recruiter will not submit your profile without explicit permission.

8. You should let the recruiter know how often you would like to hear from them for a check in.

9. You will keep your paperwork/profile current (Chapter 2).

As a traveler, you should expect and only accept an agency and recruiter that is open, honest, and will put your interests first. In return, they should expect you to be open, honest, and communicative. Whatever agreement you make with your recruiters, *honor it.* If your recruiter falls off the wagon, hold them accountable and remind them of your agreements. We all make mistakes, we're human and accidents happen, but if it becomes a pattern, find a new recruiter/agency. By the same sentiment, if you don't honor the agreement you made on a repeated basis, I can guarantee one of a few things will happen:

1. You are not going to get that recruiter's best efforts.

2. You may get pawned off to another recruiter.

3. You get blacklisted from certain recruiters or companies.

4. The recruiter won't pitch you the best contracts they have.

Completing your Profile

You've picked your agencies and recruiters. Now, it's time to utilize all the paperwork I told you to compile in Chapter 2 to build your profile with the agencies. The agencies will either request a résumé or have you fill out their application, or both, and they will ask for copies of all the documents I instructed you to collect to confirm you are a nurse and eligible to work in the US. You will be asked to complete some knowledge exams and skills checklists, which are inevitably long and tedious, related to your area of specialty. To see a sample skills checklist, please refer to the Resources section. When you finish getting these into the agencies, you will go over them with your recruiter. This will be the opportunity to sell your skills and abilities to the recruiter, who in turn will do something similar with the hospitals to which you apply. While the agency is completing their checks, your recruiter will design your profile to highlight your experiences and skills. You need to determine how much notice your permanent job needs before you leave, whether you need any time off in the first six months of traveling (for weddings, planned trips, educational conferences, etc.), and any other schedule specifics, as this will be required in your profile.

Pre-Employment Knowledge Testing

At this stage, it's worth mentioning that there may be testing administered by the facility prior to employment. I bring it up here, rather than later in the book when we're talking about starting your assignment, because it might affect whether you want to apply for a particular assignment. These tests are controversial among travel nurses and I'll explain below why I avoid hospitals that use them. Some of these tests require passing before you can start your assignment but are not administered until you arrive at the hospital for orientation, and if you do not pass the offer is rescinded and you're out of a job. Your recruiter should inform you before submission if the assignment requires such testing.

The PBDS (Performance Based Development System), created by Dr. Dorothy del Bueno to assess a nurse's critical thinking, interpersonal, and technical skills, is one such test utilized by hospitals. The test consists of videos in which the nurse is required to recognize the problem, assess what interventions are needed, what they expect the physician to order, and prioritize how and when the interventions are to take place. The travel nurse will be required to take the test that most closely relates to their specialty, but the tests available are limited in scope to adult med/surg, critical care, OR, OB, mental health, and ER.

As nurses, we know this doesn't cover all the specialties in healthcare, which is a major problem. If you're hired for telemetry, pediatrics, or rehab, you'll be required to take the med/surg test which will not prove your competency for these specialties. Or, say that you're hired for cath lab or interventional radiology, they will most likely give you the OR test, in spite of it being quite different from cath lab and IR. Some hospitals just give everyone the med/surg test as a basic nursing test, even though the nurse might have been in psych, OB, or ICU for years.

If they are going to use this as a competency-based assessment, I really think they need to tailor it to the specialty that the nurse is hired for, that they are competent in, and that they have been practicing in. Hospitals often use the test as a generic catch-all to try to eliminate travel nurses that are "incompetent," for which this is an inappropriate tool. I have heard numerous stories where the first week of orientation was going great, the hospital really liked the nurse, and their professionalism and competence was being proven daily in everyday situations, and then their contract was canceled because this test said that they are "incompetent." This has happened to nurses who have been safely practicing for years, even decades in some cases. Now, the nurse has no job, but still has a lease with its deposit to pay. With that in mind, in my almost ten years of traveling, I refuse to apply for assignments that require PBDS testing. However, there are nurses who do take this gamble, and that is why some hospitals continue to use this testing system. I believe a testing system to prove competency should be in place for patient safety, but at the very least it needs to be completed before a nurse drives or flies across the country and large amounts of money are spent.

We've covered finding the agencies and recruiters to make your travel nursing dreams come true. You are now informed on how to set expectations for the relationships with your recruiters. I think you're ready to find that first travel assignment by working with your recruiters to get your profile submitted for jobs in locations you're interested in.

CHOICES

CHAPTER 5

————

Applying for Assignments and Comparing Pay Packages

Life has so many great options, but you don't have to pick what seems the best. Just pick what makes you happy and it will be the best.

Unknown

ONCE YOU'VE PICKED AND JOINED YOUR AGENCIES, the next step is to work with your recruiters to make a timeline for looking at jobs and submitting to open positions. Typically, you see openings start popping up about four to eight weeks out from their start date. Your timeline can vary depending on the time of the year, the location, and the amount of notice required at your permanent position. It's important to carefully assess all the details of open positions to ensure you're only submitting for jobs that you would accept should the information gathered in the interview, and the pay package, prove acceptable.

Assessing Jobs and Submitting Your Profile

The first step of the submission process is to find an available job that interests you. This is the point at which aspiring travel nurses ask me, "Where should I go first?" No one can answer that except you. I recommend, as a new traveler, to start with facilities like what you are accustomed to. If you've spent years in a large, metropolitan Level 1 trauma center, then work with your recruiter to find that. If you're used to a community hospital in Small Town, USA, start there. Once you've completed a few contracts and become a little more comfortable in the travel world, you can switch gears, or you can choose to dive in headfirst from small town to the large city at the very beginning. It is your travel nursing journey, and no one can give you the answers. Just do what feels right for you. However, as a new traveler, I strongly recommend being flexible regarding locations and shifts. It is the key to getting your first travel contract, which can take some time. After you have a few completed contracts under your belt, then your credibility will be established, and you can be a little pickier. Finally, after you've been in the game for 30+ contracts, done the crappy assignments and paid your dues, you can begin to write your own ticket and say, "I want to go to _____."

Some travelers prefer to give their recruiters a list of criteria and see what they have available. Others like working with agencies that provide a job board so they can see the available positions. Either way, work with your recruiters to guide you to facilities that are open to first-time travelers and are traveler-friendly, especially with your first contract or two. Before being submitted, you are going to want to think about the location and the pay package. Start by doing some research on the location. At this point, you may not know the name of the hospital (you can always ask), but you can

find out about the city. See if this is somewhere you would consider going. See if the location has housing available that fits your
needs and analyze the housing cost compared to the pay package
being offered (housing options are covered in Chapter 8: Arranging Housing for Your New Assignment). If this initial research
does not check out, don't bother submitting to the opening. If you
like what you see, give your recruiter the go-ahead to submit you.
Feel free to submit to a couple of different positions at the same
time. The most important thing is to make sure before you submit
that the location, pay, and any other information that is available
at this point, is acceptable to you. If you submit to a job and know
you don't want it, due to details which you already know, it becomes
frustrating for everyone. However, agreeing to submission is not
agreeing to accept the job, if offered. If something comes up that
you don't like during the interview, or if you find a position that
suits you better, backing out after submission is acceptable.

Once you've completed all the agencies' forms and they have
verified your license(s) and references, it's time to submit your
profile to hospitals with positions of interest to you and begin the
interviewing process. As you and your recruiter begin submitting
your profile, make sure your recruiter knows not to submit you to
any job without your permission. This is especially important if
you will be working with two or three agencies and there is a high
probability, they will have some of the same job offerings. If you are
submitted by more than one agency to the same job, the hospital
could remove you from consideration for the position altogether
because this a breach of travel nursing protocol. To help prevent
this, I keep a journal recording the details. I use a single page per
submission, so I can list what agency submitted me, the hospital,
pay package, and interview notes. There is a sample in the Resourc-

es section at the end of this book if you are considering using this method to keep you organized. When you authorize your recruiter to submit your profile for consideration, make sure they include your availability for interviewing. This is important so you can be prepared and give a great first impression. This is also important if you are a night-shift worker, so your sleep isn't disturbed, or disturbances are kept to a minimum. Also, make sure the recruiter includes in the profile any time off you will need, for holidays or appointments for example.

On the topic of multiple agencies having the same positions available, I want to warn you not to create a "bidding war" or to pit two recruiters against one another (going between agencies to get each to increase the package based on the other's offer), because the only person that will lose is you. You will lose because the recruiters will not want to work with you in the future. You will be labeled a PITA, or whatever professional term the agencies use for a difficult traveler. They will probably try to pass you off to another recruiter, who could be less helpful, less knowledgeable, and less successful. Bottom line: it just isn't worth it. However, while I am opposed to pitting recruiters against one another, I do believe in getting the best pay I can for a job. So, if there is a job you are seriously considering and multiple agencies have it, let each of them give you the pay package offer, but do not allow them to make a submission until you have the chance to compare. Once you decide on the pay package that works for you, contact the associated recruiter to approve submission of your profile, and let the others know you submitted with a different agency. The recruiters should already know you are working with multiple agencies and this will push them to give you the best offer they can from the start.

Comparing Pay Packages

When evaluating the available contracts of interest to me, I also look at the associated pay packages. Agencies provide the pay package information in different forms making it more complicated to assess: some break it down into taxable hourly, daily or weekly housing, daily or weekly meals and incidentals, and other reimbursements; others just offer the gross per week. Regardless of how the pay package is presented, you want to put it into a form of equal comparison, so you can quickly see which is offering you the best deal, especially if you are deciding between two or three great offers.

You can convert each pay package into an hourly rate or a weekly gross by using either the PanTravelers Calculator at the Professional Association of Nurse Travelers website or the Nomadicare Fair Pay Calculator (both are free to use at the time of publication). You could also divide the pay given in weekly terms by your contracted hours (36, 48) for the week; and monthly pay by contracted hours for the month based on an average four-week month (144, 192). One-time reimbursements for travel, certifications, and licensure renewal would be divided by 468 or 624 (total hours of the contract) for a 13-week contract if you are working 36 or 48 hours per week, respectively. However, these methods won't tell you what will go into your bank account, which is what I prefer.

To know what you will be taking home each week, you can utilize PayCheck City's salary calculator. Multiply your hourly rate by 36 or 48, then subtract your insurance premium (if it's through the agency) because it's pre-tax, which is the standard for most agencies. Put the total in the salary calculator, select the appropriate state, and the number of allowances you claim, to discover the total you will receive after federal and state income taxes. Then just add your weekly non-taxables to see your actual income. I use this to make an accurate comparison of pay packages because each state has different income tax rates, and some don't have any income tax (Alaska, Florida, Nevada, New Hampshire, South Dakota, Tennessee, Texas, Washington and Wyoming).

It's as simple and complicated as that. You now have the underpinnings of what it takes to assess the assignments available, get your profile submitted to your assignments of interest without being a PITA, and how to compare pay packages for the assignments. Now it's time for you to sit back, take a deep breath, and relax. Just kidding! It's time to prepare for the interview phone calls to commence.

CHAPTER 6

Interviewing with Hospitals

Interviewer: So, tell me about yourself.
Me: I'd rather not...I kinda want this job.
ANONYMOUS

ONCE YOUR PROFILE IS SUBMITTED TO ALL YOUR preferred assignments that meet your requirements, the interview phone calls will begin. Hospitals give this responsibility to different individuals or computer systems, so you could end up speaking with someone who is responsible for all the travelers at a given facility, an HR representative, or a pre-recorded set of questions. However, most of the time, you will speak directly with a nurse manager of the unit in which you will be working. While interviews for travel contracts are less formal since they happen over the phone, this doesn't mean you shouldn't bring your "A" game. When you are interviewing for a permanent position, you go to the hospital's HR department or the unit manager's office dressed in your best and fully prepared. In this scenario, they set the environment for the interview but, as a traveler, it falls on you to create a conducive environment for an interview when the phone rings. The next few tips may seem like common sense, but I've seen and heard plenty of horror stories which suggest it's worth preparing carefully for this stage. This chapter will guide you through the interview preparation, the interview flow, questions to ask, and how to do a computerized (pre-recorded) interview.

Preparing for the Interview

The first thing to do, which I mentioned in the previous chapter, is to have your recruiter include your availability in your profile so the interview can happen at a reasonably convenient time for you. This will ensure you are fully prepared and expecting the call. You should know that some interviews can happen on the same day your profile is submitted, depending on the urgency of the need at the hospital. If you know that the hospital will be calling on a certain day, please try to make yourself available. However, if they call at an inconvenient time, it's reasonable to ask for their availability and then you can call them back, or let it go to voicemail. Please don't get me wrong here: if the hospital calls for an interview and the pressing issue at hand is that they will be interrupting your television watching, turn off the television and take the call!

Next, make sure you are in a quiet area for the interview, so you and the interviewer can easily hear one another. If the hospital calls and you're out with friends at a local hangout/bar, you might want to let the call go to voicemail, and then call them back when you don't have to yell over the band and noise. This is a real job interview after all, and you should maintain a level of professionalism. With that being said, I have taken interview calls almost everywhere—the beach, a bar, girl's trips, a family vacation, the nurse's lounge at my current assignment hospital, and once even in a Vegas casino. But I always make sure to find somewhere quiet in these locations. Whatever it takes for them to hear me easily and for me to hear them without inappropriate noise in the background. Also, make sure your phone is charged and you're in a decent cell reception area. If your phone dies or the signal drops in the middle of your interview it will be disruptive, embarrassing, and could appear unprofessional. Lastly, have a notepad or journal on hand to keep a record of the interview details and a copy of the Hospital/Unit Interview Details list contained later in this chapter and in the Resources section. I didn't start taking interview calls just anywhere until two or three years into my travel career, because by then I had memorized all the questions important to me.

The Interview

Most travel contract interviews will start with the interviewer introducing themselves and the details of their hospitals and units. They will generally cover the most common types of patients, diagnoses, nurse-to-patient ratios, charting system, and devices utilized on the unit. Then, it's time to talk about you and your background and experience. Remember, they should have your résumé, so they know the basics. Give them what a résumé can't. For example, when I am interviewing for my CVICU/CTICU positions, I start by breaking down my type of CVICU/CTICU experience, because not all units are created equal. I let them know I have experience caring for immediate post-heart surgery patients, heart and lung transplant patients, major vascular surgery patients, mechanical circulatory support patients, and patients requiring continuous renal replacement therapy. Then, I dive into the specific brands of devices that fall into the categories and the cardiovascular intravenous drips I am accustomed to working with. This all ensures that the interviewer will know without a doubt if my skills fit their unit's needs or not. The bottom line is that you need to highlight the specific skills and experience that apply to your specialty. Thus, I suggest sitting down and making a complete list of procedures, devices, drugs, and any other relevant experience that may help you stand out. Keep this with your interview journal to ensure it can be easily referenced. This interview flow is the most common I have experienced over the years; semi-formal, but professional. Occasionally, I would come across an interview that would stick to a more formal flow, like an in-person interview for a permanent staff position including behavioral interview questions, like the ones listed below in the Computerized Interview Platforms section.

Once the interviewer has given their speech and you've dazzled them with your interview skills, now is the time to ask questions that have not yet been addressed. Below, I have compiled a list of questions I've learned to ask from experience in the industry. Most of these are often answered by the interviewer's speech at the start of the interview, but it's worth having them in hand in case there are any gaps that need filling. While some may not apply to you, the list can help get you thinking of possible questions specific to your needs. Your questions can be anything pertaining to the hospital or unit, from patient care issues to aspects of the job such as scheduling. This is also the time to discuss any time off you require during the assignment, which should have been included in your profile submitted by the agency. Questions regarding the compensation package and anything related to the services provided by the agency should be taken up with your recruiter.

I know that many books on the interview process advise you to have at least a few questions to convey your interest in the position, show you did your research on the facility, or something like that. Is it a good idea? Yes, probably. However, I've never been one to follow the rules, and if I honestly don't have any questions for my interviewer, I won't ask any. I tend not to waste my time, or anyone else's. But, even if you don't have any questions, you should still respond with something that does convey interest, if you genuinely want the position. If they come to the point where they ask if I have questions, and I don't because they have answered everything during their presentation, I will usually respond with something like, "No, I think you've covered everything I need to know. It sounds like it's an environment that I'm used to and would feel comfortable working in, and I would love to hear back from you if you are interested."

When you respond with questions, or just a statement of interest, be prepared for what will most inevitably follow: a job offer. It is important not to accept the position on the phone at this time. A good reply is, "I appreciate the offer; I will discuss it with my recruiter who will be in contact with you." This way, you are not put on the spot and you are able to analyze the information gathered and other options that you have before deciding.

Questions to Ask Your Interviewer

HOSPITAL/UNIT DETAILS

- What is the name of the interviewer and their position?
- What is the location of the hospital?
- How many licensed beds in the hospital?
- How many floors are there?
- How many beds are in the unit?
- What is the type of patient population?

- What is the parking situation (ease and cost of parking)?
- What type of orientation is required (length of time, both hospital and unit orientation or just unit)?

STAFFING

- What is the nurse-to-patient ratio?
- Will I be asked to float?
- What shift are they looking to fill?
- Is overtime often available?
- Who will be scheduling me?
- Is it possible I will ever be canceled on a shift? How often?
- What would be the likelihood of extending the assignment?

WORK ENVIRONMENT

- What nursing management model do they use on the unit?
- How many travelers are currently working on the unit?
- What support staff are available (nurse aides, lab techs, RT, PT)?
- What computer charting system is used?
- What is the required color of scrubs?

Computerized Interview Platforms

Another type of interview utilized in the travel industry to streamline the process for both the traveler and facility is the computerized pre-recorded interview system. This system allows the traveler to complete the interview process at a time that is convenient for them, even if that's the middle of the night for my fellow night-shifters. There are two parts to the pre-recorded interview process. First, a link will be sent by your agency for you to answer a brief questionnaire about your past work history and clinical experience. Second, you will receive a notice to call into the interview phone line. Once you do this, you will input your unique identifier and will be asked to respond to pre-recorded questions that are determined by the facility. The recording will ask the question and you will be given a few moments to think about your answer before you provide your response. The response time for each question is usually two to three minutes. Your recruiter should let you know upon submission to the facility if they utilize this system. Yes, it is weird the first few times you complete an interview using the system. It will always feel a little awkward and unnatural working on a timer and responding to a recording rather than a human being. However, the key is to have your answers ready to roll before the questions are even asked.

Through my own personal experience, and the experiences of fellow travelers, I have compiled the most common questions asked via the computerized interview system.

- Talk about a time when you felt your patient load was too heavy. What did you do about it?

- Tell me about a time when a patient was dissatisfied with their care. How did you handle that situation?

- Give an example of a time when you went above and beyond for a patient.

- Talk about a time you worked in a fast-paced setting. How do you prioritize tasks while maintaining excellent patient care?

- Talk about a time when you had not communicated well. How did you correct the situation?

- Describe a situation when you had to work closely with a difficult coworker. How did you handle the situation? Were you able to build a relationship with this person?

- Give an example of a time you had to interact with a hostile patient or family member. How did you handle the situation and what was the outcome?

As you begin to prepare your answers to these questions, I suggest the STAR method to ensure you respond thoroughly but remain concise to stay within the allotted time. STAR stands for Situation, Task, Action, and Results. For situation, paint an extremely specific picture by addressing the exact circumstances, who was involved, and why the situation happened. For task, explain your role in the situation and the challenges being faced. For action, discuss, very specifically, the actions you took, step-by-step, to resolve the situation. For results, clearly detail the results of your actions and highlight your strengths. You can also add what you learned from the situation if time allows. The entire interview, whether telephone or computerized recording, averages 15 minutes, and the most I have ever experienced is 30 minutes for a live person telephone interview. This was when the interviewer utilized behavioral questions in addition to the standard flow described above.

After the Interview

Once you have completed your interview, whether recorded or live via telephone, you'll want to contact the recruiter that submitted you for the position. I let the recruiter know how I feel, or the vibe I got from the interviewer, and if I want to remain in consideration for the job. If you don't feel like the position is right for you once you have completed the interview, even if the pay package and location was what you wanted, let your recruiter know so you don't waste your time or anyone else's, and you will be removed from consideration for that position. I have never experienced any issues with turning down a job. It is part of the process of finding travel assignments. If your recruiter makes you feel guilty for not wanting a position after interviewing, remove the recruiter from your list. This goes back to Chapter 4's expectations discussion; they should never make you feel guilty.

When I call my recruiter after an interview, I have my interview journal with me to ensure that all the details discussed will end up in the contract if I take the assignment. Especially, if I requested and discussed time off with the interviewer and they said they could accommodate the request. Once you have completed your interview(s) and debriefed with your recruiter, your recruiter will contact you again with any offers that result from the interview(s). Then you will need to evaluate if the offers meet your needs and desires. In the next chapter, you are guided through the process of reviewing contract offers, confirming contract details, and giving notice of intent to leave your staff position.

CHAPTER 7

—

Accepting the Offer and Giving Notice to Your Staff Position

Choose a job you love, and you will never have to work a day in your life.
CONFUCIUS

ONCE YOU HAVE COMPLETED YOUR INTERVIEW, whichever type, consider how you feel about the facility based on everything you've learned in the interview, from your recruiter, and the pay package information provided. It may take interviewing with a few hospitals before you get an offer for your first contract, so don't be discouraged. It's the nature of the beast. Once you've been offered a position, you'll need to formally accept it, if you want it, and give notice to your staff position. You would think a simple yes and sign the contract would be all it would take to accept the offer but, like everything else in travel nursing, there's more...so much more.

Reviewing and Confirming the Contractual Conditions

When the offer is made and presented to you, you need first to make sure it has everything that was discussed and agreed upon between you and the hospital, and between you and your recruiter/agency. This is where the profile submission journal comes in handy with recording the details of your interview. Review the offer/contract for information, such as the start and end dates, the facility and unit, the shift type (day, night, mid-shift, etc.), the hours per shift, the shifts per week, and hours per week. Next, of course, is what it's all about...the money. Confirm your hourly rate, on-call rate, charge rate (on the chance you may be in charge), call-back rate, holiday rate, and overtime rate. Also, make sure to confirm your meals and incidentals rate and lodging subsidy rate (if you chose to find your own housing), or that you have agency housing.

If your contract is a guaranteed hours contract, carefully read the fine print regarding how guaranteed hours are calculated and paid. The common guaranteed hours contract rule is that the hospital can cancel you up to three shifts (36 hours) without pay per 13-week contract, after which you are paid at your hourly rate for any subsequent hours canceled. If these details are not included, call the recruiter and find out. If you have requested time off during the assignment in advance, and the hospital agreed, make sure it is in the contract. That is the only way the hospital will be held accountable for giving you that time off. If your recruiter/agency agreed to reimbursements for certifications, licenses, travel to and from the assignment, or anything else, make sure that it's there in writing with the amount stipulated. Lastly, if there was anything else agreed upon, make sure it's in writing. If it is not in the contract, it's not guaranteed, so get your recruiter to include anything that was discussed during the interview. If, after discussion with your recruiter, the items are not included because the hospital refuses or another reason, you have a choice to reject the offer or accept it without the stipulations you discussed.

Contract Cancellations

Another critical topic regarding contracts is their cancellation by the hospital. This is unusual, but there an increase in cancellations early in the coronavirus pandemic because of a reduction in the performance of elective procedures. Other reasons a hospital might cancel a contract are lack of finances, lack of patient census, or lack of necessary skill and ability on the part of the nurse to fill the need for the hospital. Hopefully, you will never have a contract canceled on you, because it is a massive waste of time and money for all parties involved. As good practice, you should always find out from your recruiter the hospital's cancellation policy. Are you given two weeks' notice? Do you still go to work for the duration of the notice, or do you immediately stay at home? Do you still get paid for those two weeks if notice is given? These are the types of questions I would ask ahead of signing the contract. Once you confirm all the 't's are crossed and the 'i's dotted, you can put your John Hancock on the signature line.

Giving Notice to Your Staff Position

When you resign from your job, it's essential to do so as gracefully and professionally as possible. Please don't give the single-finger salute as you say, "I quit!" or "Kiss my @$$, I'm done!" Yes, I have done this in my past, and I still have those thoughts from time to time in crappy contracts, but I've learned to keep my mouth shut... *mostly*. But, back to the proper way to quit. You want to leave the right way in case you find that travel nursing isn't for you and you want to return to a staff nursing position in your hometown. So, give adequate notice to your employer, write a formal resignation letter, and be prepared to move on when submitting your resignation.

Giving adequate notice is one of the best ways to retain your ability to be rehired. Two weeks' notice is the standard practice when resigning from a job but, in some cases, you may be required to give more. If you have an employment contract or union agreement that states how much notice you should give, abide by it. If you are uncertain of the time requirement, ask someone in HR at your facility or contact your union representative.

Try to give your notice in person. It's always a good idea to keep it positive when you talk to your boss – even if you don't feel that way. Your resignation letter and in-person conversations should contain an explanation as to why you're leaving (to pursue travel nursing), the date you are leaving, and a thank you for the opportunity. Have a copy of your resignation letter ready to provide to your boss during the meeting. The letter should include your official notice, a specific date for your anticipated final day of employment, your contact information, and any other information relevant to your departure. The date included in your resignation letter will be used as your official termination date and accrued compensation and benefits, if any, will be calculated as of that date. A copy of the letter should also be provided to HR to cover all your bases (a letter of resignation sample for both hard copy format and e-mail format is available in the Resources section.) Even if you've worked for the facility for a long time, you can't predict what will happen when you resign. Your manager may ask you to leave immediately, stay longer, or reconsider your decision entirely. The best way to deal with this uncertainty is to prepare for every possibility.

You've got your travel gig and its start date, and you know when your last day is at your staff facility. Now, it's time to prepare for life on the road. You'll need to find housing, pack up your stuff, and make the trip to your assignment destination. The next three chapters will cover these topics in detail.

CHAPTER 8

▬

Arranging Housing for Your Assignment

FINDING NEW HOUSING AND SETTLING DOWN INTO A new place every few months can be stressful for some and thrilling for others. Personally, I go nuts if I don't change my surroundings occasionally, so this suits me well. Your key decision will be to use agency-provided housing or take the housing subsidy and secure your own. There are many different variables to consider that could point you in either direction. This chapter will go through how to choose between them, the benefits and downsides, and how to navigate these pathways efficiently and with minimal stress.

Choosing Between Agency-provided Housing and Finding Your Own

These questions below will help you work out which type of housing best suits your temperament and situation.

1. **Do you have the necessary funds for securing your own housing?** If you want to secure your own housing, you must de-

termine whether you can meet the financial obligations. If you're very flexible and willing to rent a room in someone's home, or if you have family or friends that you can stay with in the area, then this option could be highly affordable and financially feasible. If you're utilizing extended stay or similar type accommodations, then you just need to make sure that you have the cash or credit available to pay for the accommodations until your first paycheck comes in. These housing options tend to charge your debit or credit card weekly. Your first paycheck will typically be deposited on the second or third Friday of your contract, depending on whether your agency pays weekly or bi-weekly. If you're only willing to stay in an apartment, then you have to pass the credit check and produce a minimum of the first month's rent and the security deposit. If your finances are not adequate to handle any of these options, then it's best to focus only on agency-provided housing rather than wasting your time on anything else.

2. **Are you willing to dedicate the time and energy to researching and securing your own housing?** The positives of doing it yourself are that you get to pick your own place, choose your price point, pocket the extra cash from the subsidy, and you get to choose your arrival and departure dates. For control freaks like me, this is the only way. Pocketing the difference between the stipend and your housing costs can add up fast, especially if you live with a relative or friend in the area or split the rent with another traveler. By choosing the arrival and departure dates around your contract, you can give yourself some time to explore the location without the distraction of work. However, as with all great things, there is a

downside. Actually, there can be a few. It isn't always easy to find a place for the exact dates you require and for only three months at a time, especially in more rural areas. But I do have a list later in this chapter to help with your search for any area. Sometimes, you'll have to set up your own utilities, cable, and such, if it's not included in the rent. If you don't find an inclusive place, you will have to remember to cancel/disconnect when you move out, which adds an extra layer of responsibility. If for any reason, you have to leave the job before the end of the contract, whether it's canceled or you quit, it may not be as easy to get out of paying for the housing. The last worry is possible housing scams. I have provided a list of common signs of housing rental scams below to help you avoid them, but they can still sneak through the cracks.

3. **Do you prefer having control over the decision of where you stay?** It can be nice having everything done for you. You don't have to do homework to find the right place at the right time; there are no credit checks, deposits, monthly rents, and no setting up and canceling of utilities. There can be a lot to love about other people doing the legwork. You get to travel light, show up with only your clothes and toiletries, and just go to work. Simple as that. But, in the end, it means someone else is controlling your living arrangements, and they may not know or care what you like and need to be comfortable and happy. So, my fellow control freaks, beware of agency-provided housing. If you know that having the final say on your home is essential to you, and you may end up feeling aggravated and shortchanged by agency-provided housing, then it might be best to bite the bullet and spend the time and effort

getting the right accommodation for you. Remember, with agency-provided housing, you don't have the option of pocketing the extra subsidy money, and arriving early and leaving late at your location to enjoy the area may not be an option.

Like with every choice in life, there are positives and negatives to agency-provided housing and finding your own. I will now provide you with more detailed information on each option, so you can decide what is best for you.

Agency-provided Housing

Agency-provided housing is particularly beneficial for first-time travelers. All you have to do is throw your clothes and toiletries in your suitcase(s), depending on the way you pack, hit the road or catch a plane, show up at the assigned housing, unpack and go to work. This simplicity is very appealing to those new to travel nursing, especially given the amount of learning along the journey. It's one less thing to worry about. This is what I did for my first contract many, many moons ago. When you go with agency-provided housing, the housing coordinator or recruiter will be responsible for finding you a place to stay for the dates you are on assignment, with two added days at the beginning and at the end of the contract allowing you time to move in and out. The housing is generally a studio or a one-bedroom apartment with basic furnishings: a queen bed, dresser, nightstand, dining table with two or four chairs, a sofa, a loveseat or chair, coffee table, end tables, a few lamps, a standard 32-inch TV and stand. These are usually the basic packages you will find from any rental furniture company—nothing fancy. Some agencies automatically provide housewares, while with others, you must request it. Housewares are the linens for the bedroom, bathroom, and kitchen along with silverware and dining ware and, lastly, the cleaning necessities (a mop and bucket, a broom and dustpan, a vacuum, etc.). I always asked for housewares, as it cuts down on the items I need to pack. The size of the one-bedroom apartment largely depends on where you are traveling. If the hospital is in a densely populated metropolitan area, you may be looking at a studio without a lot of legroom.

Conversely, if you will be working in a rural area, you can expect your housing situation to be a little roomier. The entire one-bedroom apartment I was given in the Texas Medical Center of Houston for a contract at Memorial Hermann could have fit into just the living room and kitchen of the one-bedroom apartment I was provided in Little Rock, AR. If your contract is less than the traditional 13 weeks, your agency may place you in extended stay-style accommodations due to the short amount of time in the area and minimum lease terms at most apartment complexes.

While taking the agency-provided housing means you lose some control over where you live on assignment, it doesn't mean you can't make requests for your living arrangements. I recommend you make a list of all the important items to you in your housing and then prioritize them. When you speak to your recruiter or housing coordinator, request only the top three or four things. You are more likely to get what you want with a few requests than if you give them a long list of demands. For example, when I do use agency-provided housing, I always make sure housewares are included because I love to cook, and I don't want to have to pack up my kitchen to take with me, nor do I want to have to buy the houseware items I'll want to use for every assignment. Also, I must always have a washer/dryer in the apartment rather than the complex. I don't do communal laundry...I don't know how the rest of the apartment community lives, so my clothes aren't mingling. As you can see, my requirements are simple. Keep that in mind when you make your list and prioritize the things that matter most to you. Be realistic with your requests.

If you have a traveling partner with four legs, let the agency know that, too, so that they can find pet-friendly housing. There are usually breed and weight restrictions with dogs and, generally, separate pet deposits that the agency may have you pay. If they are a registered support pet, make sure you have the paperwork available for your agency and the housing representative, so you won't have to deal with that headache. If you have a pet, consider that they may need more than two days before the contract starts in the new environment to help them feel comfortable and safe. It's worth asking if you can have a few extra days for this purpose. They may be able to accommodate your request but be prepared for a charge of some sort on your first paycheck. Also, if you have a human traveling partner, whether it's your spouse, family member, friend, or a fellow traveler, let them know, especially if you need two bedrooms rather than one. Again, you may have to pay the difference between the housing allowance and the two-bedroom unit's cost. Regardless of your needs and wants, let your recruiter or housing coordinator know when you are accepting the assignment, so they have as much time as possible to make it all happen, and you can start your contract on time.

You'll typically be contacted by your recruiter or housing coordinator one to two weeks before starting your assignment with the information about where you will be living. They will provide you with the name and address of the apartment complex and your specific apartment, along with the name of the property representative to contact. When I receive this information, I ask about what is included in the apartment, so I can start to plan what I need and don't need to pack, and whether I need to set up internet or cable, etc. Another question I always ask is whether there is a monetary cap on utilities and, if so, what the amount is. If there is a cap, then you can plan as to what extra financial obligations you might have if you are someone that likes your housing extra cold or hot, depending on the season.

Then, I begin my research on the apartment complex and the area. With the name and address of the complex, you should be able to find a website and satellite map of the place. The complex's website will always give you beautiful, professional photographs which may not accurately reflect the reality on the ground. It will also list what amenities are available in the apartment community. A satellite map will give a view of the surrounding area and the parking situation. The last search you should do is the crime rate for the area. Usually, the local police department has a crime map on their website covering the crimes from the last year. This will give you an idea of the safety of the area you'll be living in, as well as the areas of the city where you're safe to wander and where you want to avoid. The other option is getting a report from CrimeMapping.com. If you find the housing is in an unsafe area based on this research, let the agency know immediately and share with them the proof you've found.

Unacceptable Housing

Most of the time, the housing is in good areas close to the hospital at which you'll be working; but remember, your recruiter and housing coordinator are generally not from the area you're going to be working, so they don't know. The only way they learn about good and bad apartment complexes and areas is from the travelers themselves. If you find that you are being housed in unsafe or unacceptable conditions, you must stand up for yourself. I'm not talking about an apartment that doesn't have the pool or balcony you requested, but one that you feel puts you in danger in some way. I'm talking about drug arrests, murders, rapes, and similar crimes in the complex or in the surrounding area. This information can be found utilizing the search methods I detailed in the above paragraph before you even arrive at the location. Once you arrive, if you find your apartment without safety items like smoke detectors or a fire extinguisher, or you find pests or rodents:

1. Take pictures with date and time stamps for proof.

2. Go to the complex office, inform them of the problems, and share the proof. They should have someone deal with these issues within 24 hours.

3. Share the proof with your agency. If the problems are not corrected by the complex management within a reasonable amount of time, ask your agency to relocate you. They'll either move you or light a fire under the complex management because they don't want you not working (they don't make money). If the agency won't move you or pay for you to use an extended stay hotel while the problems are being fixed, or the problems are not being addressed by the complex management, and your living situation is genuinely unacceptable, then walk away from the job. Your safety is worth more than one assignment. Oh, and don't forget to find a new agency to work with, not that you would forget after something like that. But don't worry. I've rarely seen housing that was unacceptable, and I've never seen an agency refuse to relocate someone with proof of unacceptable conditions.

Accepting the Housing Subsidy and Finding Your Own

The other housing option is to take the monthly subsidy (sometimes called an allowance or stipend) provided by your agency in place of an apartment. This is for people who prefer to find their own accommodation, plan to live with friends or relatives, have a secondary home in the area, or have an RV or camper. Whether or not you are taxed on your subsidy or the apartment provided by your agency depends on whether you maintain a tax home. The amount of your housing subsidy will depend on your assignment location, the cost of living in the area, and the bill rate. I know some travelers feel that they can do a much better job of finding a furnished apartment than their travel agency and pocket the difference between cost and subsidy. Yes, I'm one of those travelers. You do need to keep in mind that agency-provided housing does not just include the rent itself. Your agency will arrange everything for you in the way of furniture rental, utilities, and your deposit, so you need to consider these costs on top of any rental outlay to compare the two accurately. But, if you still feel the subsidy is a better deal, go for it.

Looking Out for Scammers

Before you start searching for your own assignment housing, you need to be aware of scammers and how to identify them, as this is one of the significant risks of self-securing housing. Below, I'll go over some of the biggest red flags that will help you to identify a suspicious operation.

- First, a scammer is <u>never in town</u>. Even if they set up a time for you to view the place, there's always an excuse as to why they can't be there. If they refuse to show you the place in person, it should be a huge red flag.

- They will go to great lengths to appear legitimate. They may ask you to fill out an application and will probably have a generic lease that they found online. They may even show you a picture of their passport or driver's license (which are either counterfeit or stolen).

- Look out for bad grammar, poor spelling, and strange wording choices in their literature. I've often seen them use UK English such as "colour," "labour," or "honour," and they use the word "revert" a lot instead of the word "reply." While UK English is not wrong, it just highlights the risk that the person posting is not in the US to show you the rental.

- They go straight for the money. Of course, they do...that's why they're doing it. But you have to ask yourself, "Why aren't they running a credit check or doing any tenant screenings on me?" Well, because they don't care, and there's a cost involved for them in these processes. They may ask you to fill out an application that they downloaded online (see #2) as they're always trying to appear legitimate, but never a background check. *Pro traveler tip: always try to pay for a deposit using a credit card so you can dispute the transaction (there is no legal recourse once you send money through an electronic payment system like Zelle or CashApp), and never wire funds.

- They create urgency. They will often say things like, "If you want this place, you'd better hurry up, or you're going to lose it." Don't take the bait. Sometimes they're pretty aggressive, and other times they can play it cool. Either way, if things don't add up, don't send any money—just block them and move on.

- <u>The rent will be better than the average for the area</u>. This gets your attention and keeps you hooked because you don't want to let this 'great deal' slip away. Don't ignore the basics, and don't get so invested that you're not willing to walk away.

- <u>Odd communication hours.</u> For example, you may only receive emails from them that are time-stamped between 10pm and 6am in the US time zones. This indicates that they may be on the opposite side of the globe in a country with the daylight hours that correspond with 10pm to 6am in the US. This means the person won't be showing a rental in the US anytime soon.

The bottom line: regardless of how you find your assignment housing, remember that if it sounds like it's too good to be true, it probably is!

Recommended Routes for Finding Housing

Now let's look at places where you can find housing accommodating the short rental schedule of travelers.

Furnished Finder

Furnished Finder is a short-term furnished housing provider for traveling professionals requiring stays of 30 days or more. It was launched in 2014 at the Traveler's Conference: an educational training-based conference specifically for travel healthcare professionals that I discuss in more detail in the Resources section. Furnished Finder offers a variety of properties, including rooms in homes, apartments, hotels, condos, mother-in-law suites, town-homes, etc. The service connects you directly to the property owners and managers and offers free owner verification reports, which will tell you the name of the owner on record, if there is any pending foreclosure, and other property-specific information, which reduces the risk of scams.

To utilize the free services of Furnished Finder, you just visit the website and put in your assignment location. Depending on the location, there could be hundreds of options. I don't know about you, but I don't have time to check out each listing with a phone call. Thus, I recommend completing a profile for the website, and a housing request, to find more tailored options. In the housing request, you choose move-in and move-out dates, location, number of occupants, if you are looking for a shared or private space, and if you're traveling with pets. This will give you results that should be available during your timeframe. Then, you can filter the results by other requirements such as parking, private entrance, pool, private bathroom, utilities included, etc. Finally, include your name and contact information and complete a section telling them a little bit about yourself. In this section, I usually ask the owners to contact me via email rather than by phone since I am a night shifter. Once they've made initial contact via email confirming their rental is available for my dates, I narrow down the results to a few that interest me, and I set up times to have phone conversations/interviews to see if there is a fit. When a fit is found, I start working with the owner on a lease, deposits, cleaning fees, background check, etc. and inform any others I interviewed with that I have found other arrangements. Make sure that you get everything in writing, as it covers you and them in the instance of a dispute. I have utilized this service for housing in Arkansas, California, and Kentucky.

Zeus Living

Zeus Living is corporate housing, furnished for stays of 30 days or more. They have homes and apartments that are fully stocked with the basics for daily living like linens, cleaning supplies, shampoo, conditioner, body wash, and lotions. All utilities are included in the rent, including Wi-Fi and HD cable TV. The kitchen comes equipped for everyday cooking and entertaining, including kitchen linens and small appliances, pots and pans, chef knives, wine glasses, serving dishes, and utensils.

Zeus Living has accommodations in the San Francisco Bay area, Los Angeles, Seattle, Washington, D.C., Metropolitan New York, and Boston. When you're ready to search the homes, all that is needed is your required dates and the city. Then, you can narrow by price point, the number of beds, whether pets are allowed, laundry in-unit, etc. Once you've narrowed down the results, you can view the floor plans and do a 3-D tour that is just like being inside the property. What you see on the tour is what you get, and I'm speaking from experience. I utilized a Zeus property during one of my California contracts.

The results from your search will include the total price for the time of your rental request, as well as a payment schedule. Once you've decided on a place, select and book by accessing and signing your lease online. Zeus provides digital leases with clear terms. Once you handle the lease, you can pay online using a credit card or bank transfer for free. You can also easily split payments between multiple people if you are sharing it with other travelers, which is what I did. The home will have a smart lock or a lockbox with the house keys, which you will get the code to on the day your lease starts so that you can move in on schedule. Zeus properties have on-call technicians for when things go wrong with applianc-es, plumbing, heating, ventilation, or air conditioning units.

Airbnb

I think we all know about Airbnb. We've either used it for a vacation ourselves, read about it, know someone who has used it, or someone who lists accommodations on the site. Many only think of Airbnb for a short stay—a weekend or week-long vaca-tion—but they also offer listings that are strictly for 30 day stays or longer. Sometimes, when using Airbnb, you will be "competing" with short-term vacationers because the rental owner allows both short- and long-term stays and they make more money by booking lots of short stays rather than one long-term stay. However, they are often open to having people for longer stays as it provides them with security and less cleaning outlay, and thus there is often a discount.

With every Airbnb search, you can filter down to your perfect fit, whether you are looking for particular amenities or a maximum price. Once there is a list of filtered results, you can see pictures and reviews from past renters. The listing host is generally avail-able by multiple contact methods for questions or concerns, and Airbnb offers a safe way to pay for your stay. They also have a re-fund policy just in case the rental is not as described or pictured, unclean, unsafe, etc.

Extended Stay Hotels

Some travelers like to use extended stay hotels for the first week or two of a contract to find out about the local area. This gives them the time to rent a place they've seen firsthand. Others use extend-ed stay hotels for their entire contract. Most include pet-friendly rooms with Wi-Fi, fully equipped kitchens, flat-screen TVs with cable, laundry facilities, pools, a fitness room, and grab-and-go breakfast. They usually offer a once-a-week cleaning service with the rental. Also, most agencies have discounts with extended stay hotel brands, so ask your recruiter or housing coordinator if they have a code that you can use when you book. The national brands I have found in my searches are Extended Stay America, TownePlace Suites and Residence Inn (both by Marriott), InTown Suites, Hawthorn Suites by Wyndham, and Candlewood Suites. I have stayed at Extended Stay America and Residence Inn facilities in my travels and had no problems or complaints with either.

Facebook Groups and Pages

Facebook has numerous groups and pages posting rentals for travel nurses. They are easy to find by using the search feature. I used the term "travel nurse housing" and found more than 60 groups and pages. Some specialized in certain areas or cities while others boast specialty housing types like tiny houses, recreational vehicles parked on a plot of land or campground site, or in-law suites. This is just another channel through which to find what works for your personal situation. I have never used this avenue for my housing search, but I have worked and spoken with travelers who have, as well as Craigslist, without any issues. Keep in mind the "Lookout for Scammers" list as you use these, as there are extremely limited resources available to help confirm the legitimacy of housing posts.

RV Life

For those of you who already do plenty of traveling or camping and own some sort of mobile living unit, I highly recommend this from a financial perspective. Some travelers have an RV that they move from assignment to assignment, while others have smaller mobile living arrangements like a converted van or trailer. This is a good option if you are looking to travel long-term or if you already have a mobile living arrangement. However, if you are not sure if travel nursing is something you will be doing long-term, the initial investment of an RV or truck and camper may not be worth it just for these purposes.

Mobile living arrangements help alleviate the struggle of packing up all your belongings, finding housing, and moving every 13 weeks, but it may not be the best option for everyone. It should allow you to make more money per contract since you can mostly pocket the housing subsidy. If you already own a camper or RV, I believe it's worth trying it at least once to see if you can tolerate being in a camper for 13 weeks. It's one thing to go on a trip for a week; it's quite another to live your daily life in an RV for 13 weeks. Another thing to consider is the possible distance from the site to your contracted hospital and how easy it is to travel from one to the other. Most RV sites are a little off the beaten path because most who utilize campers do so to enjoy nature. While I am not an expert on RV and camper living, there are many Facebook pages, blog sites, and books on this subject, and I think it's wise to utilize these resources before you take the leap. These are just a few housing ideas that either I, or close traveler friends, have experienced. Many other resources exist for travel housing options, and I have listed them all in the Resources section.

If your housing, whether self-secured or agency-provided, doesn't include Wi-Fi, television services, telephone services, or similar services that are important to you, you will want to make sure you have an appointment booked before your assignment begins to have these items installed or set up. To find out service providers available at the location, I usually go to allconnect.com. On the website, you provide the address of your rental, then a list of service providers is shown. I usually only need the internet because I get my television through apps like Sling, Hulu, and YouTube, which is the case for most travelers. Honestly, I have these appointments setup shortly after learning the address of my residence when I use agency-provided housing. The housing I find through Airbnb, Furnished Finder, and the like have always had internet included.

Insuring Your Belongings

One final consideration while covering living arrangements is insuring all the belongings you decide to take with you while traveling. If you're a current homeowner, your homeowner's insurance covers the structure and the contents of your home at the address listed on the policy, but you will want to review the policy to determine if the contents are covered if temporarily housed at another location (your assignment housing). The same question should be asked if you're a renter. A renter's insurance policy covers the contents at the address listed on the policy, but does it include contents temporarily housed at another location? You'll want to find out if contents are covered when split between two rentals if you are planning to maintain your rental in your home state while you're on the road. My RV and camper readers, you too, will want to determine if your RV/camper insurance covers the stuff inside or just the RV/camper itself.

Once you've read through your policy, I would make an appointment with your insurance agent to confirm everything and discuss your plans. If, while having the discussion, you and your agent de-termine a little extra coverage is needed, just know that a $50,000 renter's insurance policy costs $20 or less per month. You shouldn't need that much coverage once you read the next chapter unless you have expensive taste. The total cost of the everyday items which travelers bring with them is $7,500 or less. The most important thing is having your belongings covered in the unfortunate event of a fire, water leaks, or severe weather. It is stressful enough to recover from such events without adding the financial burden of replacement.

We've covered a lot of information in this chapter, but you should be able to determine if agency-provided housing or find-ing your own housing is the path for you. You know how to iden-tify unacceptable housing and housing scams, and you now have several channels to find assignment housing, with more listed in the Resources section. Lastly, ensure your belongings are financial-ly covered so you can focus on the fun instead of worrying about something happening. This brings us to the topic of packing up your insured belongings for the journey.

CHAPTER 9

———

Packing Up
Your Life

I'm looking forward to the trip, but I hate the packing!
C. M. BUCCERE

O
N MY FIRST TRAVEL ASSIGNMENT, I ALMOST packed my whole house and took it with me to Missouri because I didn't know what to expect. The good news is that you will get to know what to expect because you bought this book. There is one golden rule to remember when moving: **always ask what is included in the housing.** This is essential to helping you prevent over- or under-packing and is true whether it is agency-provided housing or self-secured housing. Over the years, I have found ways to condense my packing down to ten, 18-gallon reusable plastic storage bins and a guitar case that fit in my SUV and hold everything I want and need to be comfortable. You are probably thinking that is a lot of stuff, and it probably is for some travelers. But this is my life; I live on the road 10 to 11 months of the year, and I want my familiars and comforts with me. Some travelers pack less, and

others more, as with everything else in life, to each their own. My personal rule is if it doesn't fit in my vehicle, it doesn't go. Like with everything, you will find what works for you over time. However, you need to know what the *necessities* are for the first contract as a baseline. As I mentioned in the housing chapter, furnished for some agencies means furniture only, while for others furnished means turnkey, which includes everything, so you only need your clothes. Therefore, it is important to confirm *exactly* what is provided.

How Should I Travel?

Before you start packing, you need to decide if you are flying or driving to your assignment because each method determines how much you can bring. If you are driving, you will always have transportation available, be able to bring more items, and it's often easier if you have a pet because you don't have to navigate difficult airline rules requiring immaculate pet health records and the correct paperwork. However, long multiday drives can be exhausting for you and your pet, and in major metropolitan areas, parking can be an issue. Flying offers fast travel, giving you more time at home before leaving for your assignment, and it's perfect for those who hate long road trips. It also offers the ease of just packing the necessities—clothes and toiletries—ridding you of the hassles of packing and unpacking large amounts of belongings for each assignment. However, you must deal with public transportation, car rental, or coordinating the delivery of your vehicle with your schedule, if you decide to ship it, all of which can be steep. Let's not forget there is little room for anything other than clothes and toiletries in your suitcase, which limits comfort items (unless you're paying the extra baggage fees, which can get pricey, too).

Shipping Your Vehicle to Your Assignment

For the travelers who want to fly but also want their vehicle with them, there is the option to ship your vehicle. I have investigated this option multiple times before, but I found it to be too much of a hassle for my purposes. However, I've met travelers who do this exclusively when making a cross-country trip for assignments. Many vehicle shipping companies exist; just do a Google search for "car shipping." I've listed the ones I found during my investigation in the Resources section. You can also check with your agency if they have the names of autotransporters. They may also be able to get you a discount from the company, so it's worth investigating. As you do this search, you need to be aware there are car shipping *companies* and car shipping *brokers*. The companies have truck drivers that work exclusively for them and possibly even own the trucks used. Car shipping brokers are like travel healthcare agencies—they post on a job board which vehicles need to be transported, then the truck drivers decide what jobs they want to do. Regardless of whether auto shipping company or broker, most do not guarantee they can ship vehicles with items packed inside if you choose to put items in your car to limit the amount you take with you on the flight. Several I spoke with said it was up to the individual truck driver as to whether they take the vehicle with items packed inside. Another factor is the delivery timeframe of your vehicle. The prices for shipping are dependent on your vehicle make and model and the speed of transport from origin to destination. The cheapest method allowed a week for a cross-country delivery, but there was no guaranteed delivery date, and that would have cost me $800, not to mention the ticket price of the flight. Without the guarantee of them moving the vehicle and the variability of delivery time, I said nope.

Making Your Packing List

Once you decide on your method of travel, you will need to pack accordingly. Before you start packing, consider how many days it will take you to get to your assignment destination. The first thing you want to pack is your suitcase with daily items while on the road so that everything you need is easy to access. Then you can pack the rest. Here is an extensive list of housing items to help you decide what is essential to take. It's also a useful reference when speaking with your recruiter, housing coordinator, or landlord to mark off what's included in your housing so you can see what essentials to bring.

Bedroom

* Sheets
* Pillows
* Blankets, comforter/duvet
* Alarm clock
* Clothes hangers

Bathroom

* Towels
* Washcloths
* Shower curtain and hooks
* Trashcan
Hairdryer
Brush
Comb
Razor
Make-up
Toothbrush
Toothpaste

Kitchen

* Cooking utensils
* Dishes and glassware
* Silverware
* Pots and pans
* Dishtowels
* Potholders
* Coffeemaker/tea kettle
* Microwave
* Toaster
Crock-Pot
Food storage containers

Living Area

* TV
DVD/Blu-Ray player
Streaming device
Small radio or digital speaker
Gaming console

Home Cleaning

* Laundry basket
* Small vacuum
* Broom/dustpan
* Mop/bucket

Indicates items generally included with housing

Electronics

Cell phone
Camera
Camcorder
Laptop, tablet
Wi-Fi router, if not included
Printer
Batteries and chargers
Flashlight
E-reader

Clothing

Scrubs
Work Shoes
Dressy and casual clothes
Workout clothes
Sleepwear, bathrobe
Shoes
Sweaters
Coats (rain and winter)

Work Items

Stethoscope
Penlight

Workbag for all your nursing paraphernalia
Phone numbers for nurse manager, new facility and your recruiter
A copy of your travel nursing contract
First-day instructions Timecards
Copies of nursing license, credentials, and documentation requested

Personal Items

Driver's license
Car registration and insurance papers
Social Security card
Major credit cards, debit cards
Personal photographs and mementos

Day Off Activities

Swimwear
Beach Towel
Hiking Shoes
Bicycle
Musical instruments
Scuba gear
Skis (snow or water)
Rollerblades
Boat
Motorcycle
Jet ski

Yes, you read that right. I have known those who brought their big toys for days off. Whatever works for you. Just remember that you will have to find somewhere to park it because not all apartment complexes or residential areas allow parking for those items

Now you have this long-ass list, but it still doesn't have everything you might need because some of us ladies need a curling iron or flat iron, and some of you guys need your beard trimmer. And some of you will be traveling with a pet; don't forget their essentials. Now that you can see how overwhelming it can be let's break it down into manageable parts for smooth sailing. You already know to ask what is included in the rental, which will cut down on what you must bring, so the rest is all about you. Consider what you use and do regularly. We all have different lifestyles and daily habits. As such, it's a good idea to make a list of items that you use regularly over a one- to two-week period. We're all creatures of habit, so this list should encompass the majority of what you'll need to maintain your current lifestyle while on assignment. This list should include your pet(s) and their needs because I hope you are feeding and giving TLC to your four-legged family members daily. If you're not, we need to have a chat. The bottom line: take whatever you need to enjoy yourself. I'm sure you haven't decided to become a travel nurse purely to work 36 hours a week in a new place without enjoying everything the location has to offer. This means bringing what you need to have fun and take part in your hobbies on your days off.

If you're not the best list maker because you're always forgetting to add something, there is an app for that, just like everything else these days. Back when I started traveling, we only had paper and pencil. Oh wait, the pen had been invented. The most popular packing list app is PackPoint, and it is available for Android and iPhone. It allows you to write an easily editable packing list and, once you put in your destination and the dates, it will actually give you a list for packing based on the weather at that destination for that time of year. Similar online packing list generators are Travelers Checklist, Packtor, Packpal, and SmarterTravel. Once you have your list, whether on paper or in an app, consider what can be purchased once you arrive at your destination and what must be brought from home. REMEMBER: if it doesn't fit in the vehicle or in your flight luggage, it doesn't go with you. Please also remember that anything that goes with you must also come back. Anticipate gaining a few items while on assignment and plan to leave space for these. If you can't get it all to fit for your return trip, then you might have to ship some items. It really isn't that expensive when it comes down to it, but frequent shipping can add up.

Since this is your first travel assignment, you may forget things, but you will always learn from it and will eventually know exactly what you need on any given contract. You can often pick up low-price housewares at stores like Big Lots, Walmart, or a dollar store. If it is something specific from home you would really like to have, you could always ask a friend or family member to send it to you. I do it all the time. I'm sure my mother is on a first-name basis with the staff at her local post office.

Organize and Save Space

Most travel nurses will pack more than the average traveler. After all, you'll most likely be away for at least 13 weeks, which is longer than a typical vacation. But you'll also have a limited amount of room in your car or flight luggage. That's why it's critical to organize your belongings carefully to save space. This is also an excellent habit to adopt, considering you will be going through the process frequently; making everything easy to repack will reduce the stress and time involved in moving. As I previously stated, I utilize reusable, rugged plastic totes. I have been using the same totes since I started traveling, with only two or three replacements needed when the originals have broken. They are available in various shapes and sizes, so you can find what works best for your belongings and vehicle.

To stay organized and to enable quick unpacking, I label each tote based on its associated room (kitchen, bathroom, bedroom, etc.). To save space (so I can bring more items that I need), I interfold clothing into most of my containers for cushioning to prevent fragile items from breaking. You may be wondering what interfolding is? It's just using all available space within a container because unused space is inefficient. An example of interfolding is folding your socks into your shoes, folding your clothes into the cracks between other items in the containers, and taking items out of boxes and placing them in flexible storage bags so they can be molded into an available space. I also use compression bags for soft items (clothes, towels, jackets, etc.) to remove the air and fit more into less space. REMINDER: only pack each container or piece of luggage as heavy as you can carry over some distance because you may be going up and downstairs at your assignment housing.

Change of Address and Mail Forwarding

When you travel, you will need to decide what to do about the mail that you usually receive. There are several options. The first is to have the post office hold your mail. However, the USPS (US Postal Service) website states that they will hold mail for three to

30 days. Obviously, this is not long enough for your typical 13-week assignment, but it might be okay if you are doing a four-week assignment. Your second option is to change your address to your new assignment address. USPS.com now allows you to change your address online. If you choose this option, I suggest switching to electronic billing, which will deliver the bill directly to your inbox, so it doesn't fall through the cracks as you move from assignment to assignment. Then, set up automatic electronic bill pay through your bank, so you don't have to worry about forgetting. Another option is to leave your address as is and have a trusted friend or relative check it and let you know about any important stuff. The last option is a virtual mailbox, which is a service that receives and processes your physical mail. They scan the outside of the mail you receive and send the visual via message to your phone or email. Then you can choose whether they open and scan the contents for your viewing, forward it to you where you are, or schedule a pickup if you are close to the location of the virtual mailbox service. Multiple companies offer this type of service with varying price plans. I have listed several in the Resources section.

I hope this chapter gave you some insight into the options for travel to your assignment—flying with or without vehicle shipping and driving. It should have begun to shed light on how to pack based on your method of travel and to make the most of the space you have available. Finally, I hope it gave you an idea for dealing with your mail, so you don't miss any bills or important communications. Now it's time to get ready for your physical journey.

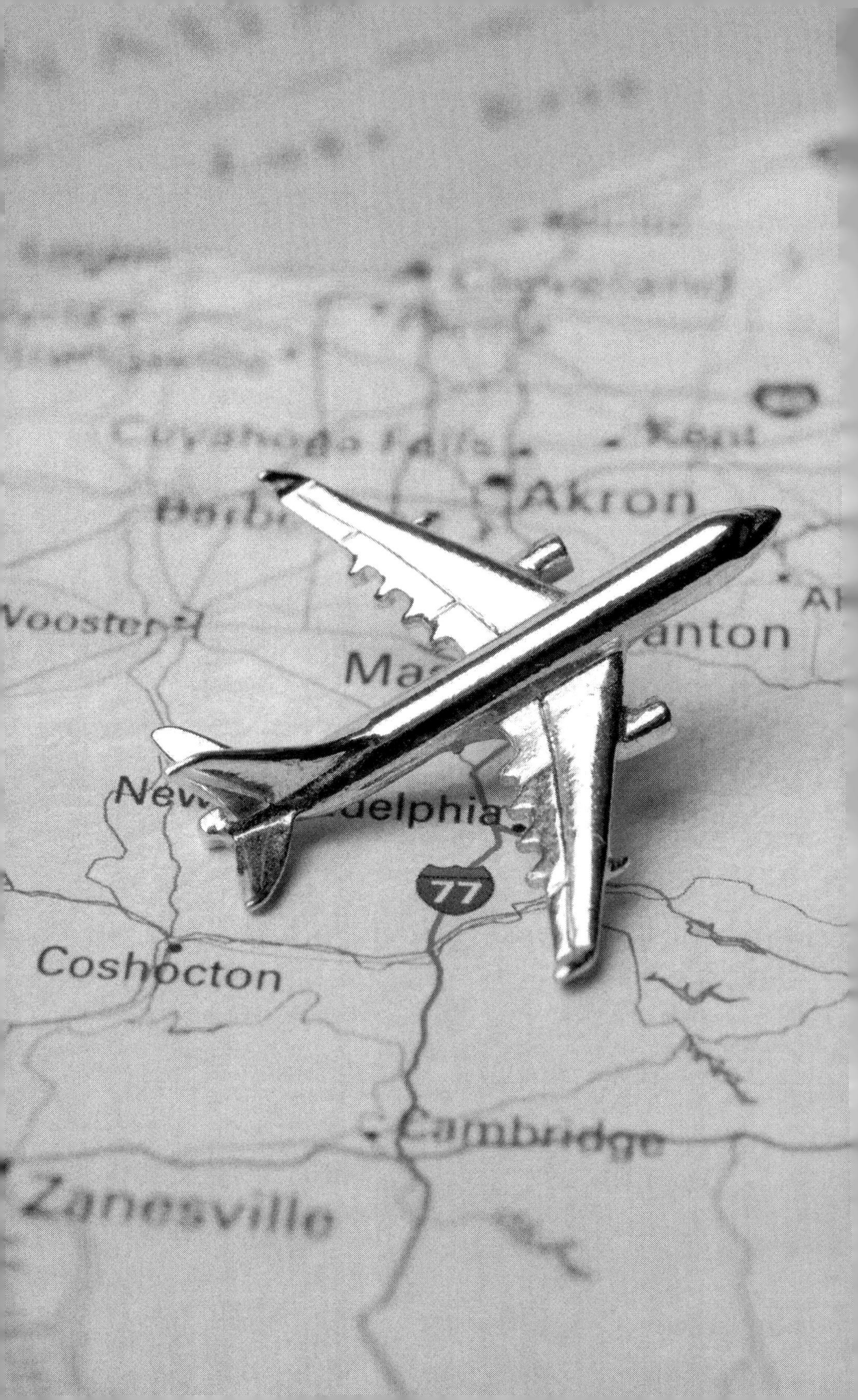
Akron
77
Coshocton
Cambridge
Zanesville

———

CHAPTER 10

Getting Ready for the Journey

The journey of a thousand miles begins with one step.
LAO TZU

BEFORE YOU HIT THE OPEN ROAD WITH ALL YOUR belongings in the back, your road trip playlist turned up, and your cell phone docked in the center console, make sure that you are fully prepared for the journey ahead. This includes getting your vehicle ready and creating a clear plan for your road trip or arranging your flight and transportation if you're flying. This might not seem like a priority, but planning an efficient and problem-free trip will ensure that you are ready to work when you arrive at the other end. One critical thing to remember before you begin: *make sure that you are cleared to start.* I wouldn't want you to drive or fly a few hundred or, even worse, a few thousand miles, just to find out you can't start because of a technicality with credentialing.

Getting Your Vehicle Ready

About a week before you plan to leave, take your car in for a full service. Nothing can spoil your road trip faster than being stuck somewhere you would rather not be, waiting for your vehicle to be repaired. When you take it in, ask the service center representative to check all fluid levels, tire pressures (including spare), wheel alignment, engine and cabin air filters, brakes, windshield wipers, engine belts, and anything else you think might cause you problems. I recommend having a jumper pack and knowing how to use it. Jumper cables are good too, but you won't always have another vehicle on hand to use, thus the jumper pack recommendation. These packs can be charged via a traditional wall plug and will jump-start a battery with terminal connectors or charge the battery enough through the cigarette lighter port to start the vehicle. The jumper pack can also charge other items with USB connections. While all cars come with a tire jack, make sure you know how to use it and that you can use it in case of a flat tire on the trip. If you have a newer vehicle that does not come with a spare tire, make sure you have the number of a roadside service provider saved in your cell phone. If you are not already a member of a roadside service plan such as AAA, OnStar, or Good Sam Roadside, consider joining one before you take off to places unknown. The simple law of averages says that if you take enough road trips, you will eventually end up stranded on the side of the road. You can avoid a lot of hassle, as well as potential dangers when you have that 1-800 number handy to connect you to reputable towing and repair services.

Getting Your Pet Ready

While you are getting your vehicle ready to roll, start getting your pet(s) prepared for the journey, too. First, get your pet used to being in the car if they are not already. Making short trips to the park, the pet store, or any new place will give you the opportunity to see how your pet responds. The test drives will let you know if the animal gets motion sickness or anxiety, which is not something you want to learn on a long road trip. While making the test drives, practice pet travel safety: get them used to being in an appropriately sized crate or carrier and make sure it's tied down. If your pet is not a carrier or crate fan, get a crash-tested harness to keep them safe in the event of an accident. The test drives are also an opportunity to reinforce their training, like safely exiting the vehicle and returning when you call. You also want them to become accustomed to visiting new places. Otherwise, new experiences may spook your pet and cause them to forget their training.

While getting your pet ready to travel, take them to the vet for a check-up. Make sure all the preventative care and vaccinations are up to date and that you have copies for proof (don't forget to scan them into your cloud storage). While you're at the vet, ask about any interstate travel certificates you may need, as well as any vaccinations or parasite prevention specific to your assignment destination. Ensure you get a large enough supply of necessary medications to cover your time on assignment. I would also recommend microchipping. If you found your pet has motion sickness or anxiety during your test drives, ask your vet for the proper medications to make the trip easier for them and you. Don't forget to grab spill-proof water and food bowls and a travel litter box for feline friends. If your cat is not already potty trained for outdoors, they won't understand outside potty breaks on the road without a litter box. If you have accepted a contract in Hawaii, which is rabies-free, be aware they have special rules to prevent the disease from being brought in. The quarantine process can be found on the State of Hawaii's Animal Industry Division's website. If you are flying with your pets, airline fees and restrictions are becoming stiffer and more challenging now than ever. Airlines now require vaccination records and a recent letter from the vet stating good health. Restrictions are placed on breed, weight, and the number of pets, and the rules vary from airline to airline. Check with the relevant airline to see if your pets can travel.

Before hitting the road, make sure your pet is flea-free. Once fleas get into a home, they are tough to get out, and no landlord will appreciate the extermination and cleaning required. Consider that cats and dogs could also scratch or knead everything in your new accommodation, leaving behind ruined furniture, baseboards, and doorframes. With a quick trip to the vet or groomer, you can have your pet's nails trimmed at a very reasonable cost or nail caps put on. I would have this done before each new move. If all else fails, consider having the claws removed permanently (I'm not a fan of the idea) but ask your vet for advice during your pet's checkup.

Lastly, make sure your dog is indoor-trained. I don't mean trained to not poop or pee in the house, which is a must. I'm talking about training them not to bark incessantly. This sounds simple and obvious, but many people didn't get the memo. It's offensive to be bothered day and night by other people's animals, and neighbors may complain to the point of you being asked to leave. Generally, a bark collar will do until the dog learns when barking is acceptable. Don't forget your pet's favorite toy to help the animal adjust to the new surroundings.

Also, don't forget to find a vet for your four-legged family member at your assignment destination and a dog walker or a dog daycare, if that is what your dog is accustomed to. It will make the adjustment easier for them. Ask your current vet for a recommendation; check out Yelp!; ask other nurses you meet at your assignment if they have a suggestion for a local vet, or, check with local pet stores.

Getting Your Road Trip Plan Together

If you're heading just across state lines, or less than a day's drive from your home, you can throw your stuff in the car and leave, no planning necessary. For the assignments that will take more than a single day's worth of driving, a little forethought and planning will make the trip more enjoyable and cut down on unpleasant surprises. As I stated in the previous chapter, you will need to pack a trip suitcase with enough clothes and toiletries to cover the trip, as well as enough food for your pet. The number of days required to get to your destination will depend on the overall miles, how many hours a day you are planning on driving, how fast you drive, the frequency of food, fuel, and potty pit stops, the weather, and, if you want to make the trip a mini-vacation.

First, use Google Maps to determine the length of your journey in hours and miles. Be realistic on drive time. When traveling with pets, don't forget to factor in time for their stops because they may need a little more leg-stretching and more frequent bathroom breaks than you. Once upon a time, I would drive 12 hours in a day, waking up before dawn to begin, but I've gotten to a point where I only travel about 500 to 600 miles a day. That's about eight hours with food, fuel, and potty pit stops. It's because I can't stand being in a vehicle longer than that, but I've also learned to slow down and enjoy the journey instead of rushing to get from point A to point B in the shortest time. I would love to say this means that I've learned to stop burning the candle at both ends, but I'm working full-time at the bedside of a busy heart and lung transplant unit and have written the majority of this book in three months, essentially working two full-time jobs. I guess I haven't learned all that much! But, back to the topic.

Next, you want to consider the time of year you are making the drive and the usual weather patterns along the route. I crossed the US in a vehicle for the first time in November 2019. I was traveling from Lexington, KY, to Napa, CA, and the shortest route would have been over to Kansas City, up to Interstate 80, over to Lake Tahoe, and down to Napa. But, at that time of year, I-80 is frequently closed due to snow and ice in Wyoming, Utah, and Nevada. If you are accustomed to driving through snow and using tire chains, you'll just need to add extra time because of the slower speeds required, but the route doesn't have to change. However, I wasn't ready to practice my non-existent ice road trucker skills, so I was willing to add a little time and distance by going the more southerly route from St. Louis to avoid the stress of dealing with ice and closed interstates. This also allowed me to see the Grand Canyon from the southern rim. I would have loved to take in the views of the Bonneville Salt Flats in Utah or the Grand Canyon from the north rim, but I wasn't risking my life for it.

Accommodations Along the Way

Knowing life doesn't always go as planned, and the weather can cause last-minute route alterations, I don't reserve my hotel rooms for the duration of the trip, just a night at a time. While I have an overall plan, I like to leave some extra time if I find something interesting to do along the way. When traveling with pets, make sure to choose hotels with pet-friendly rooms. The most important thing about keeping your pet in a hotel room is to remember to declare your pet and pay the pet deposit. If you don't, they can charge hundreds of dollars as a "fine," similar to if you were smoking in a non-smoking room. If your pet is documented as a support animal, make sure to have the documentation with you to prevent problems at non-pet-friendly hotels.

Making the Most of the Road Trip

Once I have my general route planned, I use the RoadTrippers website or app to find attractions that may interest me along the way. For example, on the way back from California, I was reminded of places I had forgotten about over the years that I wanted to see. I made stops at the Grand Canyon, Meteor Crater, the Painted Desert, and the Oklahoma City National Memorial. I spent two nights at the Grand Canyon, giving myself time to see the sunrise and set across the canyon, and spent a day hiking and a day biking the entire south rim. I spent another day hiking the rim of the Meteor Crater and biking through part of the Painted Desert. My last stop was at the Oklahoma City National Memorial, where I had the opportunity to gain a greater understanding of the 1995 bombing since it happened when I was in elementary school and too little to understand the magnitude of what happened.

In my travels to and from other assignments, I have managed to visit friends and family along the way. Some of my favorite visits are with former colleagues, if I happen to be passing through a city or town, I previously worked in. There are so many opportunities to explore, have fun, and catch up with your friends and loved ones on your way to, or from, an assignment. Rather than seeing it as a necessary chore, see it as an opportunity, and give yourself the flexibility to make the most of it.

Planning Your Flight and Transportation

For my travelers planning on flying to your assignment, I didn't forget about you. Your choice just requires a little less planning than your driving counterparts. If you are utilizing agency-provided housing, remember the earliest you can access housing is two days before the start of your contract, unless you made other arrangements with your agency. Also, keep in mind the hours of operation of the leasing office at the apartment complex to ensure they are open when your flight arrives unless you are planning to arrive early and stay in a hotel until you can move in. This obviously doesn't apply if you found your own housing and can enter whenever. While searching for your flight, bear in mind that flights get canceled and delayed all the time for various reasons, so allow for some leeway to make sure you're not late for your first day of work. Also, plan your transport from the airport at the other end if you are not renting a vehicle.

If you are planning to rent a car for your assignment, I strongly recommend reserving it ahead of time. More than once in my travels, I've gotten to a rental lot with only one car and six people at the counter; but I reserved ahead, so the car was mine. This is especially true of traditionally busy, major airport hubs. For those who are shipping their vehicle, you too, will want to rent a car for at least a few days until yours arrives. Like previous situations, check with your agency about discounts. They may have contracted deals with certain rental car providers of up to 25 percent, depending on your agency. A quick side note about rental cars: the only time I've seen car rental included in pay packages is for contracts in Hawaii, Alaska, and island territories of the US.

We've now covered arranging housing accommodations, packing the necessities, and prepping for your journey. The next steps are to move into your assignment housing and get to work at your first travel job. In the next chapter, I will cover what to do if your accommodation isn't up to par, how to make a good first impression, and making the most of your assignment location.

—

CHAPTER 11

Moving In and Starting Your Assignment

The beginning is the most important part of the work.
Plato

Yᴏᴜ'ᴠᴇ ᴀᴄᴄᴇᴘᴛᴇᴅ ʏᴏᴜʀ ꜰɪʀsᴛ ᴛʀᴀᴠᴇʟ ɴᴜʀsɪɴɢ ᴀs- signment, and you're in the midst of packing up your belongings and making travel arrangements. What's next? You've reached that moment you've been waiting for: the first day in your new location and, soon after, the first day at your new job. It's both frightening and exhilarating. The start of something new can be overwhelming, thus it's vital to plan and prepare for these first few days to ensure that they go as smoothly as possible. What if I'm missing equipment in my accommodation? What if there is a defect? What do I need to do in my first 24 hours? How can I make a good first impression when I arrive at the hospital? Let's look at this critical time period in more detail.

Moving in and Setting up

If moving into agency-provided housing, I arrive as early as I can, usually two days before the start of the contract, because that is all the agency will provide in terms of housing. This is just another reason why I prefer to take the subsidy and find my own housing. I like to give myself more time before the assignment starts. Generally, I aim for three or four days so I have more time to unpack, get the lay of the land, find all the important places, and adjust to changing time zones. When I first arrive at my accommodations, whether agency-provided or self-secured, I do a cursory walk-through to detect any significant problems or damage. This is in addition to what I covered in the Unacceptable Housing section in Chapter 8. Here, I'm referring to things like electrical sockets hanging out of the wall, exposed electrical wiring, or wet areas on the ceiling from leaking pipes or the roof. This is usually *not* the case but, if you experience this, make sure you take photos. Remember, visual proof does wonders. Then, contact the management office for your apartment or landlord of the rental, inform them of the situation, and request maintenance/repair of the problems. If your housing is agency-provided, let your agency know and forward the photos. For my fellow travelers that decide to take the subsidy and find your own housing, now is the time to pull up your big folk underwear and deal, because it's between you and the landlord (unless you utilized Airbnb, Zeus Living, an extended stay hotel, or some other short-term rental agency). If you used Airbnb, you could deal with the rental owner first. If the problems aren't fixed, Airbnb has a refund policy (again, visual proof works wonders). For those who chose Zeus Living, call into the maintenance service line. For extended stay hotels, let the front desk know and maintenance will handle it, or they will place in you a different room. If the problems are significant enough, I recommend a hotel for the night, giving you the chance to get a decent night's sleep and deal with everything the next day.

If you feel comfortable with moving in, get your stuff out of your car and start unpacking. As you unpack, do a reasonably detailed assessment of the place for the move-in condition report so you're not held liable for any previous damage. Within the first two or three days, run the dishwasher, washing machine and dryer, try each burner of the stove and the oven, and run the hot water tap in the shower/tub to check they are in working order, if not, get them fixed by the owner or management agency. Also, make sure to take pictures, as I've already stated, with a date and time stamp as proof. Most travel agencies provide a move in/move out inspection form, but the rental complex should also have some method to document initial problems with the unit. If you discover any damage, you can either ask that they be repaired or just note it on the move-in inspection form. Ask for a copy of the document and keep it in your cloud storage. You will want to repeat this inspection when you move out to cover liability issues regarding damage.

Also, as I'm unpacking, I try to make everything as homey as possible for my comfort and my usual lifestyle, so my brain is in the right frame of mind to start my contract. While unpacking, I make a shopping list of anything the rental doesn't have that I like to have, but didn't bring with me, as well as groceries, and necessary pet supplies (especially carpet cleaner with a scrub cap for accident spots caused by your pet as it becomes accustomed to the new environment, and carpet sprinkle powder to keep pet odors to a minimum). This helps ensure the return of the housing deposit. The next day, I go to a store where I know that I can find all the items on my list, such as Walmart or Target. I make a practice trip of getting to the hospital from my rental, to determine the time required and see the parking situation, so I'm not late on Monday morning for orientation. With my GPS frequently telling me to make U-turns, I locate a gym, a tech store like Best Buy, shipping places (UPS/FedEx), and the nearest post office to my temporary residence. Sometime in the first weeks, you will need to have communication services setup, as covered in Chapter 8.

Making a Good First Impression

I arrive early on the first day of hospital orientation, giving myself 30 minutes to ensure I'm not late getting where I'm supposed to be. I make sure I have a copy of my first-day instructions and any paperwork requested by the facility. The hospital orientation may be strictly travelers, or a traveler/staff mix. The first people that will be easy to get to know are other travelers. Experienced travelers are used to being the outsiders and enduring the same challenges and obstacles; we stick together and try to help one another. With everyone you meet that day, take the time to really face them and shake their hand during introductions. This will help you to make a great first impression and maybe give you the opportunity to find a nurse or two you have more in common with than just nursing. Now that we have experienced a pandemic, you may have to do the chicken wing elbow bump to limit germ spread and wear masks, which limit view of our facial expressions. But make sure to square your body with theirs, look them in the eye, and speak as clearly as you can through your mask.

On your first day of unit orientation, bring something in that reminds them that you're happy to be there and ready to help. The first thing I want to make clear is, you do not have to bring "presents" for your coworkers on your first day, or on any day of your contract. I never have, and I've done fine on my assignments. This suggestion is merely to help break the ice with staff and maybe find a friend or two to associate with outside of work to combat loneliness while on assignment. One travel coworker-turned-friend loved to bake. He would use recipes he wanted to try or already liked and bring in the results to work, which he called his "friend bait." His personality did not require "friend bait," but it served to spark conversations, even if they were just about the food and recipe.

When I talk about "breaking the ice," I'm not only speaking of getting to know someone. I am also speaking of the "ice" that may have been created at the facility by interactions with previous travelers, or the staff's perception of travel nursing overall. You never know what experience the staff has had so far with travel nurses, or what perceptions or preconceived notions they have based on what they've heard through the grapevine. The staff may have experienced travelers that were always trying to change things, know-it-alls, lazy, complainers, and those that weren't team players. Or staff nurses may have a chip on their shoulder because they believe we, as travel nurses, are unfairly overpaid and should bear the burden of higher acuity patients as a result. You may experience the complete opposite: staff nurses who love travelers, have found them extremely helpful, want to hear their travel stories, and think they are the most wonderful people in the world. Whatever situation you walk into, let them know immediately that you are there to do your best to help.

Laura Latimer, with Nomadicare, accomplishes this with a coffee cup, pens, and a flyer. Laura loves coffee, so she gets a mug with an inspirational quote on it and fills the mug with retractable "click" pens that she gets from the dollar store. Laura prints a flyer that has her picture on it and some introductory text: "Hello! (hospital or unit name she's going to be working in). I'm Laura. I'm gonna be the new traveler here for 13 weeks. I am so excited to be here to help you guys the best I can. Looking forward to getting to know each of you. Please feel free to take a pen, because you can never have too many pens, and say hello when you see me. Here is my face." There's an arrow pointing to her image. She puts these at the nurses' station or in the lounge, or somewhere easily visible. She does this everywhere she goes to give the best first impression, before they even meet her. This might not be your style, but hopefully this will provide you with inspiration for something that fits your personality. However, none of it is necessary. Rarely have I ever had problems getting along with the staff. I have experienced cliques and exclusion at a few assignments, but the staff usually gets along with me and wants me to stay, even if it is just to ease their patient-load burden. In the unlikely event that things don't go as planned when you start your new assignment and you are feeling like an outcast among your coworkers, remember two things:

1. You can do anything for 13 weeks

2. Your coworkers are only 36 or 48 hours of your week (but that can take a toll).

You've got your belongings in your temporary housing, you're unpacked and, hopefully, all comfy and cozy to your liking. If you brought a furry family member along, hopefully they are adjusting to their new environment and you've had the opportunity to find an acceptable veterinarian practice to provide them care while you are on assignment. You're meeting new people at your job, who you may or may not be getting along with, but either way you need to enjoy your time away from work. In the next chapter, I'll cover how to make the most of your days off at your assignment location.

CHAPTER 12

━━

Combating Loneliness and Making the Most of Your Assignment Location

Victory comes from finding opportunities in problems.
Sun Tzu

IN THE INTRODUCTION, I MENTIONED THAT ONE OF the biggest challenges which travelers can face is the feeling of loneliness or homesickness, even with Facetime, Instant Messaging, Skype, Facebook, email, and the presence of your faithful furry companion. I mentioned that you must be comfortable in your own company as a travel nurse. In the beginning, you won't know anyone unless you happen to be in an area with family, friends, acquaintances, or if you're traveling with someone. You need to be able to keep yourself entertained, and it's important to make the most of your downtime. If you're not having fun while living in your new town or city, you're not making the most of the opportunities that travel nursing affords you. Surely new experiences were near the top of the list when you decided to sign up for this new way of life? However, this takes a little effort and creative thinking when you're so far away from home and familiar faces. Make time to consider what you might want to do on days off and plan out ideas and options that will make your 13 weeks memorable and rich.

Party Plans on Assignment

Make the effort to plan your days off. This is your opportunity to be near new experiences – make the most of it. You will need to do a little research on activities that are available in the area. The best place to find this information is the local tourism office, or the city's tourism website. Both will provide free information and materials about hiking, fishing, boating, local and state parks, educational centers, restaurants, museums, movie and performing arts theaters, festivals, and events. Another option is a bookstore's local travel section, where you can usually find books about local tourist attractions, activities, and points of interest. Below are some ideas and examples to help keep you occupied during the length of your assignment.

1. *With several days off in a row, plan a trip somewhere, whether local, a few hours away, or across the country.*

2. *Find out about local cultural experiences, such as local theater productions, museums, art galleries, and festivals.*

3. *Take a day trip to a local state park for fishing, hiking, or biking, if these are your niche.*

4. *Find out about local cuisine and hotspots and go out to dinner at a sit-down restaurant.*

5. *Live music and concert lovers, visit Ticketmaster, Live Nation,*

StubHub, Vivid Seats, etc. to see if any of your favorite music acts are playing locally during your assignment.

6. *Use meetup.com to find people locally who have the same hobbies or interests and find a gathering to attend.*

7. *Explore Facebook groups for travelers in the area to arrange meet-ups and sharing of information and stories.*

8. *Ask your coworkers about spots that only locals know about so you can discover the hidden gems.*

This list is meant to spark ideas that you can tailor to your likes and personality, but here is how I've incorporated some of these things into my travel lifestyle. During my first assignment in the fall of 2011 in Springfield, MO, I made the short drive to Branson, MO, for the numerous variety and musical shows the city has to offer, as well as the fall and Christmas festivities in the town and at Silver Dollar City. My second assignment took me to Kansas City, where I made time to visit the World War I Museum and the Harry S. Truman Presidential Library and home. My next assignment was in Lawton, OK, for the summer, where I gained more knowledge of Native American culture by visiting the Museum of the Great Plains, Comanche National Museum and Cultural Center, and Fort Sill Museum. While there, I took a day trip to Wichita Mountains National Wildlife Refuge in Cache to hike and visit with a few buffalo, and another day trip to Medicine Park to hike, shop, and relax. My next assignment took me to San Antonio, TX, for nine months, so I took in everything—the Riverwalk, the Alamo, all the missions, the San Antonio Stock Show and Rodeo and the accompanying concerts, Six Flags Fiesta Texas, and even caught a Spurs home game.

Fast forward to fall 2018 and, while in Louisville, KY, I started adding overnight trips or vacations while on assignment when I had several days off in a row. Twice, I went to Nashville. Once, I happened to catch the 93rd birthday celebration of the Grand Ole Opry, which included multiple concerts with some of my favorite country stars and the chance to go backstage. I also had the opportunity to visit a traveler friend I worked with in Little Rock in 2017, who was on assignment at Vanderbilt. We met at The Valentine, where we hung out with some of her coworkers and friends to watch the LSU/Georgia football game and caught up with each other's lives. The second trip to Nashville in May 2019, I saw comedienne Carol Burnett at the Ryman Auditorium. Another fun trip was to Lexington, KY, to catch Alabama and Trans-Siberian Orchestra in concerts before Christmas 2018. My best trips while on assignment have been to Vegas—three times in five months in 2019. The first was to enjoy July 4th by the pools at Caesar's Palace and catch a Reba, Brooks & Dunn concert just because I had four days off. The second trip was in September for the Travelers Conference held at Bally's. I met up with traveler friends from around the country, but I was most excited about catching up with my favorite "friend bait" baking traveler. The Travelers Conference is covered in the Resources section at the end of the book. The third was a pre-Christmas trip with a travel nurse co-worker turned friend.

Other fun closer to Louisville included concerts by Tracy Lawrence, Pam Tillis, Mannheim Steamroller, and Cher during the fall of 2018 and winter of 2019, and several plays at the Actors Theater. I went on some of these trips and outings alone, and others with coworkers-turned-friends, but either way it definitely kept away the feelings of homesickness or loneliness, which I really don't encounter much after all of these years. If you develop a friendship at work, take a leap and ask them if they want to accompany you on one of your planned activities. Making new friends takes courage but taking that first step might make the rest of your time there so much more enjoyable. The worse thing that will happen is they'll say no. In that case, please don't stay at home – follow through on your plans regardless. Not going out because you don't have a companion to go with is the quickest route back to that homesick, lonely state of mind. For example, I wanted to see the Dracula play that was being performed at the Actors Theater. One coworker mentioned it at work, so I brought up my interest and ended up going with three or four coworkers and having dinner before the show. Had this not been the case, I still would have marched my ass to that theater and enjoyed the show.

Everyday Living on Assignment

Other ways I have combated the feeling of loneliness while on assignment, when partying wasn't an option, is continuing to live my life as if I were at home in Louisiana. For you, that might involve shopping, hiking, biking, running, doing yoga, video gaming, cooking and baking, or fishing. It's about continuing to do the day-to-day things you love to do, regularly. Personally, I love massages, facials, manicures, and pedicures. I have these done regularly at home and I still do when I'm away. Because of this, I maintain a membership with Massage Envy and find one close to my assignment location. For the manicures and pedicures, I must find a place at each assignment, but trying out all the salons keeps me busy. If you like to stay active and work out, go find a gym. I maintain a membership with Planet Fitness because they have centers all over the country. If they don't have a gym within reasonable distance of my assignment location, I put my membership on hold and use a local gym that offers month-to-month plans. The other thing I like is playing my guitar. In each town or city, I find a music store as they usually have information about gigs, jam sessions, and other musical hangouts. This way, I'm around my musical people. You can do the same for your hobbies, which is where the meetup.com comes in again.

Don't forget that you can arrange to meet up with friends and family in your new location, or you can travel to them if you have enough time off. During assignments in which I complete multiple extensions, I regularly plan time to return home to visit family and friends, and just be in my culture and the comfort of my own home. In the past, I have met family at big hotel resorts for Christmas when I was only able to get two or three days off work. In this way, I could still see them when I couldn't go all the way home to Louisiana, and they appreciated the opportunity for a Christmas vacation where there was little to do except relax and enjoy the local area.

There are many ways to combat the loneliness; you just have to know what works for you. If you are fortunate enough to have a travel partner, whether it be a spouse or a friend that's a fellow travel healthcare worker, then that can be a built-in homesickness, loneliness breaker. The essential point of all of this is: be who you are and what you are, no matter where you are. If you absolutely require your friends and family in close proximity for entertainment and daily comfort, travel nursing may not be for you.

CHAPTER 13

—

Ending Your Assignment (or Extending It)

A good traveler has no fixed plans and is not intent on arriving.
LAO TZU

YOU'RE NOW OFFICIALLY A TRAVEL NURSE! YOU have weeks of experience on the job and a good idea of whether you want to continue being a rolling stone. If you want to keep going, you'll need to think about the next step: securing another contract or a new assignment. This might be (and often is) extending your current contract, which is usually straightforward. Or, if the hospital no longer needs support or you're ready to roll on, you'll need to return to the job postings and work with your recruiter to explore new opportunities. It might even be that you want time off before you jump headfirst into the next travel adventure. Below, I'll guide you through these various pathways.

Extending Your Current Contract

The most uncomplicated contracts to secure are extensions of your current one. About four weeks into your assignment, start thinking about whether you like the hospital, the area, and if you want to stay for an extension. Contract extensions are offered if the facility has a continued need, the required budget, and has been pleased with your performance. The offers are made somewhere between the seventh and ninth week of a traditional 13-week contract, so if you have been considering an extension since week four, you'll know if you want to stay or not when the offer is made. However, if you like a facility and are sure you would like an extension (depending on compensation), I recommend contacting your recruiter as soon as possible. Be clear that you're not accepting an extension, if offered, but you want to get the compensation details ironed out so that you're ready to go without surprises or delays should the opportunity present itself. Taking this step early in the contract helps you to establish a plan, so that you're not scrambling at the last minute to negotiate the extension or find your next assignment.

Negotiating a Contract Extension

There are several important variables to keep in mind when you're negotiating a contract extension. First, extensions require minimal effort for both you and the agency—no profile submitting, coordinating compliance, or engaging in a plethora of other time-consuming activities. Second, the agency should incur much lower compliance and credentialing costs than they did on the original contract. Third, the agency will not incur any non-billable orientation expenses typically charged by the hospital for orienting the agency's employees. Finally, be mindful of the fixed costs that the agency incurred on the first contract, such as travel subsidy and license reimbursements, which usually isn't required on an extension. All of these variables represent costs that the agency incurred on the first assignment but stand to avoid on the extension. In addition, it's most likely that the bill rate will remain unchanged for the extension of the contract, unless the original was offered at a premium or crisis rate and the extension is offered at the lower standard rate, or if the original was at the standard and the hospital increases the bill rate as a result of need or season. As a result of this knowledge, you should be negotiating with the understanding that more money may be available, but not *always*.

The agency may not be able to pay additional money for the extension because they offered you a great deal initially to get you to accept with the hope you would extend, giving the agency a chance to balance out on the extension. Another reason could be that they have bonuses and/or other perks already built into the contracts. If this is the condition, then it's fair to assume that the savings are being utilized for you. With every contract or extension, you'll question if you're getting the best deal but, given the number of agencies, the competition is intense. It's reasonable to believe you're getting the best the agency can offer, but there are still a few bad apples spoiling the experience for some, so you should always negotiate. If you feel you're being shorted, let your recruiter know you're going to explore contracts with better compensation at other agencies. Sometimes you have to remind your recruiter that you work with multiple agencies and that they could lose you. This may be all it takes to improve your compensation, if it's truly possible, because your recruiter will not want to lose you, or encourage you to work with another agency, as this will ultimately affect their pay.

If you and your agency can agree early in the contract on extension compensation, then you will be ready with an answer by the seventh to ninth week, when the official extension offer is made by the facility (assuming nothing has changed at the facility or with the compensation package from when you first discussed it with your recruiter). When you receive the offer, pay attention to the extension terms because they may be different from the initial contract terms. The time of the extension can range from four to another full 13 weeks. Make your recruiter aware of any time off needed within the period of the extension. Also, now is the time to switch from agency-provided housing to the housing subsidy, or vice versa, if you want (this is only allowed between contracts or extensions, not mid-contract.)

While we are on housing, if you self-secured housing, don't forget to let your landlord know you would like to extend your rental, if you want to stay there for your extension. If your accommodation has already been rented for your contract extension dates, it is time to begin the housing search again like in Chapter 8. But, this time, you have a head start because you are in the area. You'll know staff nurses that may have a room to rent, other travelers that may be leaving and if their rental is available, and you'll be familiar with the location, so you are more aware of where you want to live and where to avoid.

Finding Your Next Assignment

If, by week four of your contract, you know you will want to move on or the extension compensation terms aren't for you, let your current recruiter know, as well as your other recruiters. Now is the time to start working with more agencies if you opted to start with one and find others as you went along. If you are already working with three at this stage, now is the time to update your profile with the other two to include your first travel assignment information. Also, you will need to give them contact details for a reference at the facility. Then, you will begin the process of submitting your profile again, interviewing, and getting your compliance together. Don't forget to inform your recruiters of any time off you will need in your next assignment and your expected start date, based on the end of your current contract. If you have done as I suggested and copied and saved every compliance item from your first assignment, you should have almost everything you need. Most hospitals require most of the same documents, with few differences. I can't tell you how much time and headache I've saved myself over the years having copies of compliance documents.

Taking Time Off

I have frequently mentioned "taking time off," so let's cut to the chase. Taking time off between contracts/assignments is one of the most significant benefits of travel nursing (in my opinion). Theoretically, you can take as much time off as you like. However, there are factors you should consider. If you are extending a contract at a hospital, it's ultimately up to the hospital how much time you take, as they may need unbroken support if they're in dire need of coverage. However, hospitals are, typically, pretty flexible. The best course of action is to discuss your requested time off for between contracts and extensions directly with your unit manager or scheduler, but, as with your first negotiation, make sure it ends up in the contract to hold the facility accountable, if you are looking for less than three weeks off. However, if you are taking time off between ending a contract at one facility and starting at another, you can take whatever time you like. You just need to stipulate your available start date after your time off to the agencies.

Your agencies will want you back to work immediately, regardless of whether or not it's an extension or a new contract. The agency only makes money when you're working, as I explained in Chapter 3. Their ideal scenario is to have you working 52 weeks a year, and thus they'll try to persuade you to take less time off; but they can't force the matter. However, keep in mind that, if you aren't working for the agency, they're unable to provide their services to you because they're not billing a hospital for your services. That means no health benefits or agency-provided housing or housing subsidy. Different agencies are going to have different policies for dealing with this issue. Let's take a look at each of these services.

Medical and Health Benefits During Time Off

In many cases, medical benefits are paid on a monthly basis. For example, if the agency paid for the benefits on the first of the month, then they're going to run through to the end of the month. If your contract ends in the middle of the month, then you'll still technically be covered until the end of the month. However, it's also possible for the benefits to be paid based on your contract's start and end date. In this case, the benefits would end on your contract's end date. For example, if your contract started on March 15th and ended on June 15th, then it's possible that the agency began paying monthly premiums on March 15th and will therefore end the benefits on June 15th. So, what does this all mean for you? Well, first it means that you need to ask your agencies in advance how they handle this, if you want to take time off between contracts. Again, different agencies will utilize different methods. Many agencies will be happy to pick up the cost for a week or two if that's what they need to do to secure another contract with you, or if you've already agreed to another contract that will start within a month of your previous one ending. My current company continues coverage if you begin another contract within 24 days from the end of the last contract. The missed premiums from the time off are divided up over the first few paychecks after returning to work. However, if you do not return to work in 24 days, the insurance coverage retrospectively terminates at the end date of your contract. Others may request that you pay for the insurance coverage yourself. In any case, when making your decisions about time off, you should always consider the effects of COBRA and HIPAA's Creditable Coverage rule. Your agency will have policies and information about these.

Housing During Time Off

Housing is involved only if you are taking time off between an initial contract and an extension at the same hospital, or the exceedingly rare occasion you've accepted an assignment at another hospital in the same area allowing you to live in the same accommodations. In any case, housing represents a significant expenditure, and most agencies will not pick up the costs nor pay housing subsidy when you are not working (because they can't bill the hospital). If you are utilizing agency-provided housing and take two or more weeks off between a contract and an extension, you can expect either: to pay the housing bill for the time you are not working if you want to stay in the same accommodations; or, the agency will rehouse you. This means ending the lease for your current accommodations two days after the end of your existing contract and providing you with new accommodations two days before your extension start date, like when starting your assignment. Thus, you will have to pack up and take your stuff with you for whatever amount of time you take off.

If you receive the housing subsidy and choose to maintain your temporary housing during your time off, the money will obviously come out of your pocket because you will not receive a subsidy while you are not working. Thus, it's worth considering your financial situation and ability to cover the rent. Also, consider the cost of your plans for your time off. Will you be staying with family or friends, will you be on vacation and paying for hotels or Airbnb rentals, or taking a camping trip? If you determine the financial burden is too great to cover without your housing subsidy, then you will need to end your rental at the end of your contract and search again for a rental to start with your contract extension.

Time Off and Your Career

In addition to the financial considerations, you should also consider the ramifications of time off for your career. I know, I just told you a few sections back that time off was one of the best parts of travel nursing, and here I am worrying you about it! Just like with everything else in this book, I am making you aware of every possibility, so you can make the best choices for you and your career. Time off may not look so great on your résumé if it's excessive. Many hospitals require explanations of gaps in employment that are greater than one month in order to consider a candidate for a travel assignment. With this said, I keep my time off to 28 days or less, to circumvent the need for explanations that would amount to, "I was tired of the bullshit, so I needed time off." The only time I was ever questioned about time off was when it was three months, and that was because I was completing the clinical portion of my master's degree in Birmingham. In addition, the modern electronic application process utilized by the majority of hospitals for their permanent employment needs may "ding" your résumé if it includes time off. These applicant tracking systems are designed to rank candidates electronically, and employment gaps may hurt your ranking. You may be able to cite the agency as your employer and not include the gaps, but then the system may possibly "ding" your résumé for not working at a hospital or clinic. I hope this doesn't make time off seem more complicated than it actually is; you just need to be mindful of what's involved. Taking time off between contracts is common. I do it regularly; and there's usually not much to it and it has never caused a problem with me getting an assignment.

Closing Down Housing

Whether you utilize agency-provided or self-secured housing, there are a few things you need to do to ensure the deposit is returned and not give all travelers a bad name. If you used agency-provided housing, after packing your personal belongings:

1. Make sure to remove all food from the fridge and freezer

2. Run the vacuum, mop, and/or sweep

3. Clean, as best you can, any pet accident spots

4. Remove all trash.

Ensuring the agency gets their deposits back. If not, they could pass the bill on to you. Remember if you had to set up internet, TV, or other services to cancel them and return any equipment. If you are staying in the same area, have the services put on hold, take the equipment with you, and have it set up at your new accommodations.

For those who opted for self-secured housing, you most likely paid a cleaning fee and deposit. I still recommend Steps 1-4 above because if excessive cleaning is needed, the landlord or manager will keep the deposit to cover the difference between the cleaning fee and total cleaning cost. I'm sure these are obvious to you, but we all get busy or forgetful, so this is just a helpful reminder to keep you making money and, not spending it because you forgot to clean up after yourself. Lastly, let the landlord or manager know when you're out of the rental, so they can set up cleaning services, and you're not charged for the extra day(s) of stay. A quick phone call, email, or text message works perfectly.

Parting Thoughts

Well, ladies and gentlemen, we have reached the end of our time together. I hope the information I have provided you gives you the confidence to take the leap into travel nursing. Everything we have covered, you will need to repeat with each new assignment until you decide to stop traveling. As you move through the industry, you may find ways that work better for you. I would love to hear about them because other travelers may need that different viewpoint. Over the years, I have been offered very lucrative positions in all healthcare sectors, but none have been able to get me to stop living this nomadic lifestyle. It has afforded me the opportunities to see and do things I would never have been able to as a staff nurse. It also gives me more control over my professional life, allowing for a greater work-life balance. After a contract or two, you will know if this lifestyle is for you. Thank you for purchasing this book; I hope you feel it was worth your time and money. I will leave you with "The Big Checklist," which is a culmination of everything we have covered, and the Resources section full of helpful extras.

THE BIG CHECKLIST

- ◆ **Get your paperwork organized**
  - ■ I-9 documents to prove eligibility to work in the US
    - ▸ Driver's license (front and back)
    - ▸ Social security card (front and back)
    - ▸ Passport ID page
  - ■ Nursing License(s) (front and back)
  - ■ RN diploma
  - ■ BLS card (front and back)
  - ■ ACLS card (front and back)
  - ■ PALS card (front and back)
  - ■ Specialty certifications
  - ■ Vaccinations
    - ▸ MMR titer
    - ▸ Varicella zoster titer
    - ▸ Hepatitis B titer
    - ▸ Tdap
    - ▸ PPD results or QuantiFERON TB Gold blood test results
  - ■ Recent N-95 mask fit results
  - ■ Physical exam
  - ■ Résumé

- ◆ **Find an agency**
  - ■ Ask traveler friends
  - ■ Internet research
  - ■ Interview the agencies
  - ■ Nomadicare

- ◆ **Apply for assignments**

- ◆ **Interview**

- ◆ **Accept an assignment offer**

- ◆ **Give notice to your permanent position**

- ◆ **Secure housing**
  - ■ Agency-provided
  - ■ Self-secured
  - ■ Area/housing safety check

- ◆ **Pet's veterinarian visit**
  - ■ Vaccinations
  - ■ Preventative medications
  - ■ Claw care (cut and/or caps)
  - ■ Interstate travel certificates
  - ■ Get recommendations
    - ▸ Assignment location veterinarian
    - ▸ Dog care and/or walkers

DRIVING TRAVELERS

- **Get vehicle serviced**
- **Pack belongings**
  - ▸ Packing list
  - ▸ Road trip suitcase
- **Plan road trip route**
  - ▸ Time/Days needed to make the trip
  - ▸ Tourist attractions
  - ▸ Visit family/friends along the route

FLYING TRAVELERS

- **Determine access to housing for timing flight**
- **Book flight**
- **Pack belongings**
  - ▸ Number of suitcases
  - ▸ Baggage fees
- **Organize transport to/from the airport**
- **Reserve rental vehicle**
- **Find auto shipper (if shipping vehicle to assignment)**

- **Assess housing**
- **Unpack luggage and/or vehicle**
- **Find necessary places**
  - ▸ Work facility
  - ▸ Grocery store
  - ▸ General-purpose store
  - ▸ Pharmacy
  - ▸ Mail/shipping facilities
  - ▸ Gym
- **First day at work**
- **Enjoy the location and days off**

- **At the end of the 13-week assignment**
  - ▸ Contract extension
  - ▸ Find another assignment
- **Prepare for departure**
  - ▸ Pack belongings
  - ▸ Clean housing
  - ▸ Cancel services
- **Repeat list until you no longer want to travel**

Resources
Section

———

C ONGRATULATIONS! YOU FINISHED THE BOOK. Welcome to the other side! This part of the book is to help you put what you've read into practice, plus some additional information to help bring it all together.

The Required Documents for Your Profile

This is a detailed list of the basic requirements discussed in Chapter 2. This list of documents should be kept current, scanned, and saved into your cloud storage. These documents will be required by each agency and subsequently submitted to each hospital where you work. Also included are web addresses of sites to help the Non-Compact RN license holders complete the necessary fingerprinting and licensure verifications to gain license endorsements.

- I-9 documents to prove eligibility to work in the US
  - Driver's license (front and back)
  - Social security card (front and back)
  - Passport ID page
  - Other acceptable forms listed on the next page
- Nursing license(s) (front and back)
- RN diploma
- BLS card (front and back)
- ACLS card (front and back)
- PALS card (front and back)
- Specialty certifications
- Vaccinations
  - MMR titer
  - Varicella zoster titer
  - Hepatitis B titer
  - Tdap
- PPD results
  - QuantiFERON TB Gold blood test results for those who have had the TB vaccine

- Recent mask fit test results
- Physical exam
  - ▶ See your PCP before traveling—the company will provide a form for your PCP to sign, clearing you.
- Résumé

Licensing and Fingerprinting

https://www.ncsbn.org/

https://www.nursys.com/

https://www.identogo.com/

https://www.certifixlivescan.com/

I-9 Documents for Eligibility to Work in the US

LISTS OF ACCEPTABLE DOCUMENTS
All documents must be UNEXPIRED

Employees may present one selection from List A
or a combination of one selection from List B and one selection from List C.

LIST A		LIST B		LIST C
Documents that Establish Both Identity and Employment Authorization	OR	Documents that Establish Identity	AND	Documents that Establish Employment Authorization
1. U.S. Passport or U.S. Passport Card		1. Driver's license or ID card issued by a State or outlying possession of the United States provided it contains a photograph or information such as name, date of birth, gender, height, eye color, and address		1. A Social Security Account Number card, unless the card includes one of the following restrictions: (1) NOT VALID FOR EMPLOYMENT (2) VALID FOR WORK ONLY WITH INS AUTHORIZATION (3) VALID FOR WORK ONLY WITH DHS AUTHORIZATION
2. Permanent Resident Card or Alien Registration Receipt Card (Form I-551)				
3. Foreign passport that contains a temporary I-551 stamp or temporary I-551 printed notation on a machine-readable immigrant visa		2. ID card issued by federal, state or local government agencies or entities, provided it contains a photograph or information such as name, date of birth, gender, height, eye color, and address		2. Certification of report of birth issued by the Department of State (Forms DS-1350, FS-545, FS-240)
4. Employment Authorization Document that contains a photograph (Form I-766)		3. School ID card with a photograph		3. Original or certified copy of birth certificate issued by a State, county, municipal authority, or territory of the United States bearing an official seal
		4. Voter's registration card		
5. For a nonimmigrant alien authorized to work for a specific employer because of his or her status:		5. U.S. Military card or draft record		
		6. Military dependent's ID card		4. Native American tribal document
a. Foreign passport; and		7. U.S. Coast Guard Merchant Mariner Card		5. U.S. Citizen ID Card (Form I-197)
b. Form I-94 or Form I-94A that has the following:		8. Native American tribal document		6. Identification Card for Use of Resident Citizen in the United States (Form I-179)
(1) The same name as the passport; and		9. Driver's license issued by a Canadian government authority		
(2) An endorsement of the alien's nonimmigrant status as long as that period of endorsement has not yet expired and the proposed employment is not in conflict with any restrictions or limitations identified on the form.		**For persons under age 18 who are unable to present a document listed above:**		7. Employment authorization document issued by the Department of Homeland Security
6. Passport from the Federated States of Micronesia (FSM) or the Republic of the Marshall Islands (RMI) with Form I-94 or Form I-94A indicating nonimmigrant admission under the Compact of Free Association Between the United States and the FSM or RMI		10. School record or report card 11. Clinic, doctor, or hospital record 12. Day-care or nursery school record		

Examples of many of these documents appear in the Handbook for Employers (M-274).

Refer to the instructions for more information about acceptable receipts.

Sample Résumé

In Chapter 2, we covered updating your résumé with specific information detailing what hospitals are looking for in travel nurses. I've created an example to help you design yours, with a small sample of my information for each category. You can easily see my license and certifications and the types of units where I've worked. I have listed the specialty devices I can independently operate, which is important because facilities are looking for people they don't have to handhold beyond "this is how it's done here," whether that's documentation or implementation protocol. As you begin to develop your travel nurse résumé, do not be worried if it is more than a page or two. In the travel nursing world, that is acceptable; in fact, it is expected. My full travel nurse résumé is seven pages and growing.

Constance Buccere, MSN, RN, CCRN-CMC-CSC
Address, Phone Number, E-Mail Address

LICENSES & CERTIFICATIONS

Registered Nurse
California Board of Registered
Nursing,
Expires: Sep 2022, Lic#: ######

**Adult Acute/Critical Care
Nursing Certification (CCRN®),**
American Association of Critical-Care Nurses, Exp. 08/2022

**Cardiac Medicine Certification
(CMC®),** American Association
of Critical-Care Nurses, Exp.
05/2023

**Cardiac Surgery Certification
(CSC®),** American Association
of Critical-Care Nurses, Exp.
12/2023

**Basic Life Support (BLS) for
Healthcare Providers**
American Heart Association,
Exp. 04/2022

**Advanced Cardiovascular Life
Support (ACLS)**
American Heart Association,
Exp. 10/2022

PROFESSIONAL EXPERIENCE

Stanford Health Care, Palo Alto, CA
Jun 22, 2020 - Sep 19, 2020
Assignment Type: Travel Contract

Facility Type: Acute Care
Hospital
Teaching Facility: Yes
Trauma Level: 1
Total Beds: 550+

Charting System: Epic
Unit: CVICU
Unit Trauma Level: N/A
Unit Beds: 35 - 39
Caseload: 2

Kaiser Permanente, Santa Clara, CA
Mar 02, 2020 - May 30, 2020
Assignment Type: Travel Contract

Facility Type: Acute Care
Hospital
Teaching Facility: Yes
Trauma Level: N/A
Total Beds: 300 – 349

Charting System: Epic
Unit: CVICU
Unit Trauma Level: N/A
Unit Beds: 10 - 14
Caseload: 2

SPECIALTY DEVICE EXPERIENCE

- Fresenius NxStage® System
- Baxter Prismaflex and Pris-Max Systems
- Abbott HeartMate™ II and 3 LVAD Systems
- Medtronic HeartWare™ HVAD™ System
- Maquet Cardiohelp ECMO System
- Abbott CentriMag™ Acute Circulatory Support System
- Abiomed Impella® System
- Maquet Intra-Aortic Balloon Pump Systems
- Zoll Thermogard XP® Temperature Management System
- BD Arctic Sun™ 5000 Targeted Temperature Management System

EDUCATION

Master of Science in Nursing
The University of Alabama at Birmingham (August 2013)
Concentration: Nurse Educator

Bachelor of Science in Nursing
Southeastern Louisiana University (May 2008)

Pay Package Examples

Below are examples of actual contract compensation package per-centages. These are examples to compare how pay packages are broken down between exclusive and MSP/VMS contracts like those discussed in Chapter 3. I have also included the web addresses for determining your net pay and for your new friend, the US General Services Administration, which will help you to verify that your housing and meals subsidies are reasonable.

https://pantravelers.org/
https://www.gsa.gov/travel-resources
https://www.nomadicare.com/
https://www.paycheckcity.com/

Example for an MSP/VMS Contract

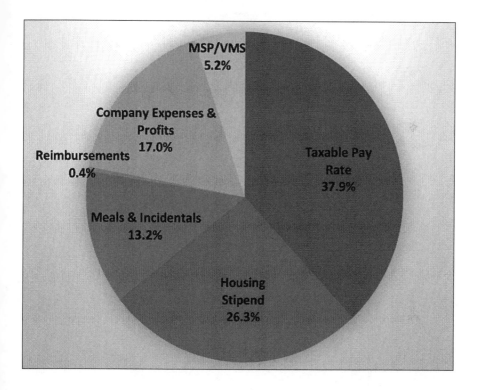

This is an example of a contract I had in Lake Charles, LA. Since this contract was within three hours of my home, I didn't require a large travel reimbursement and I had no renewals (BLS/ACLS/License) due during the contract, so the reimbursement is only 0.4 percent. I had the rest put into my meals and incidentals. The agency I used for this contract took 17 percent for fees and profits, but this contract included a VMS, so there was a 5.2 percent fee bringing the total for services by the agency and vendor to 22.2 percent.

Example for an Exclusive/Direct Contract

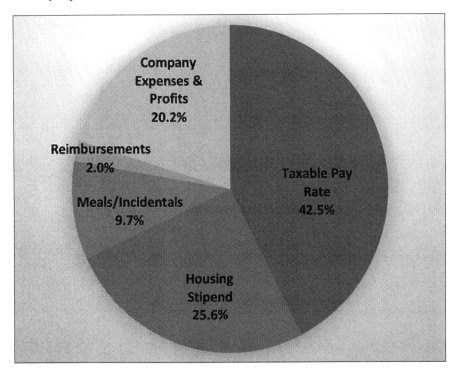

This is an example of a contract I had in Little Rock, AR. Since this contract was exclusive with the agency I used, 5 percent has not been removed for the MSP/VMS, leaving more for me. Below I have included the table from the Overtime section of Chapter 3, which correlates with these two pie charts.

	VMS/MSP ($ Per Hour)	Exclusive ($ Per Hour)
Taxable Hourly Rate	20.00	58.35
Taxable OT Hourly Rate	44.00	87.53
Housing Subsidy	15.28	14.70
Meals & Incidentals	6.94	8.36

Traveler Income Tax Help

As I wrote in the book, I am not a tax expert and definitely not a *travel* tax expert, but Joseph Smith, RRT/EA/MTax is. Joe has been a respiratory therapist for more than 20 years, with some of them as a traveler. He's also been a tax consultant for 20 years and is the founder of Travel Tax and Travel Tax Canada. These tax agencies cater to traveling professionals. Joe stays up to date with all the tax law changes, especially the ones affecting travelers. He and his team prepare returns and represent clients should there be any audits, tax controversies, or litigation for returns they prepared. I have personally used Travel Tax and have been pleased with the work.

The best part of Travel Tax is its website, which is full of excellent information and resources. Every tax year, the team creates a workbook to help you organize all the necessary documents and information for tax return completion. The website features a blog with videos and updates regarding tax law changes and all-around great money information.

https://www.traveltax.com

Travel Agency Interview Questions

These are the questions covered in Chapter 4: Researching and Choosing an Agency. This list of questions can help you decide which agency to use by determining what is important to you. Also, it can help spark other important questions not covered in this list. Lastly, I have attached the web addresses of NATHO and the Joint Commission Healthcare Staffing Services Certification.

1. What states do they have access to (have contracts available in)?
2. Do they have direct, "exclusive" contracts, or rely on MSP/ VMS for contracts?
3. How long have they been around?
4. Do they individualize pay packages (legally maxing out the travel reimbursement, meals/incidentals, and housing) based on the GSA/IRS regulations? Or are packages set by agency administration without the ability to negotiate/adjust to fit the traveler's needs?
5. Do they provide guaranteed pay or partial pay when a shift is canceled by the contracted facility?
6. Do they provide PTO/sick pay after so many worked hours?
7. Do they set up and pay for physicals, TB skin testing, urine drug screens, N-95 mask fit testing, etc. for the traveler when required by the contracted facility?
8. Do they provide reimbursements for required licensure, uniforms, CEU testing, certifications, etc.?
9. Do they provide one-bedroom furnished housing? Or do they only provide a stipend?

TRAVEL AGENCY INTERVIEW QUESTIONS

TRAVEL AGENCY INTERVIEW QUESTIONS   **151**

10. Will they reverse market for you?
11. How do they pay overtime or extra time?
12. Does the agency have someone available 24/7 for clinical emergencies or safety concerns not addressed by the facility?
13. Do they provide medical, dental, and/or vision insurance? If so, does it start on day one of the contract, or is there a waiting period? Are there options/levels to the offerings (high deductible w/HSA, PPO, etc.)?
14. What insurance companies do they use, and what is the average cost?
15. Do they have a 401k program? When can you start contributing? When are you vested? Do they match any portion of your contributions?
16. Do they offer free online CEUs?

NATHO

https://www.natho.org/

The Joint Commission Healthcare Staffing Services Certification Site

On the website, you can inquire about agencies you would like to work with to see if they meet the quality standards.

https://www.qualitycheck.org/

List of Agencies

I have included a list of agencies to help in your search for the ones that suit you best. I have not worked with all these companies, not even a third, because there are just so many. I'm sure there are even more than the ones I've listed here. Be aware that some agencies have the same parent company, which means they will have mostly the same assignments.

- AB Staffing Solutions
- ADEX Medical Staffing
- Advantage Medical Professionals
- Alegiant Healthcare Staffing
- American Mobile Healthcare
- Atlas MedStaff
- Aureus Medical Group
- Axis Medical Staffing
- Aya Healthcare
- Barton Healthcare Staffing
- Cross Country TravCorps
- Emerald Health Services
- Ethos Medical Staffing
- Fastaff Travel Nursing
- FlexCare Medical Staffing
- Fusion Medical Staffing
- GHR Travel Nursing
- Gifted Healthcare
- Health Carousel
- HealthTrust Workforce Solutions
- Host Healthcare
- Lead Healthstaff
- Liquid Agents Healthcare
- LRS Healthcare
- Malone Healthcare
- Maxim Healthcare Group
- Medical Staffing Solutions, Inc
- Medical Staffing Solutions, LLC
- MedPro Healthcare Staffing
- Nurse Choice
- NursesRx
- OneStaff Medical
- Onward Healthcare
- PPR Travel Nursing
- Premier Healthcare Professionals
- Prime Healthcare Staffing
- Prime Time Healthcare
- RNnetwork
- Supplemental Healthcare
- Tailored Healthcare Staffing
- TaleMed
- Titan Medical Group
- TotalMed Staffing
- Travel Nurses Across America
- Travel Nurses, Inc.
- Triage Staffing
- TRS Healthcare
- Trustaff
- Trusted Nurse Staffing, LLC
- Trusted, Inc
- Worldwide Travel Staffing

Skills Checklist Example

Below is an example of the skills checklist you will be asked to complete for the agencies you choose to work for. The checklist(s) you complete will correspond to your chosen specialty. These checklists will be part of the profile your agency sends to the hospital(s) you apply to. Do not over- or under-represent your skills because this is used to determine if your skill set will meet the unit's needs. Overestimation can result in the contract's termination because of a lack of ability or skills to meet the hospital unit's needs. It can also result in being listed as a "do not use" or "do not return," preventing you from applying at the hospital and the larger organization of facilities the hospital may belong to. Eliminating numerous hospitals as options for future contracts.

Medical-Surgical Skills Checklist

Key:
5 – Expert Level
4 – Performed multiple times with ease
3 – Can perform with review and/or supervision
2 – Performed once
1 – Theory/observed only
0 – No knowledge

CARDIOVASCULAR

	5	4	3	2	1	0
Abdominal aortic bypass	☐	☐	☐	☐	☐	☐
Aneurysm	☐	☐	☐	☐	☐	☐
Angina	☐	☐	☐	☐	☐	☐
Assess Heart sounds/murmurs	☐	☐	☐	☐	☐	☐
Auscultation (rate, rhythm)	☐	☐	☐	☐	☐	☐
Blood pressure/non-invasive	☐	☐	☐	☐	☐	☐
Cardiac arrest	☐	☐	☐	☐	☐	☐
Cardiomyopathy	☐	☐	☐	☐	☐	☐
Carotid endarterectomy	☐	☐	☐	☐	☐	☐
Central Lines	☐	☐	☐	☐	☐	☐
Check pulses/circulation	☐	☐	☐	☐	☐	☐
Congestive heart failure (CHF)	☐	☐	☐	☐	☐	☐
Doppler	☐	☐	☐	☐	☐	☐
Femoral-popliteal bypass	☐	☐	☐	☐	☐	☐
Myocarditis	☐	☐	☐	☐	☐	☐
Post acute MI (24-48 hours)	☐	☐	☐	☐	☐	☐
Post angioplasty	☐	☐	☐	☐	☐	☐
Post cardiac cath	☐	☐	☐	☐	☐	☐
Post cardiac surgery	☐	☐	☐	☐	☐	☐
Telemetry Basic 12 lead interpretation	☐	☐	☐	☐	☐	☐
Telemetry Basic arrhythmia interpretation	☐	☐	☐	☐	☐	☐
Telemetry Lead placement	☐	☐	☐	☐	☐	☐
Permanent Pacemaker	☐	☐	☐	☐	☐	☐
Temporary Pacemaker	☐	☐	☐	☐	☐	☐
Thrombophlebitis	☐	☐	☐	☐	☐	☐

Questions to Ask During the Hospital Interview

These are the questions I have learned to ask from experience, if not answered by the interviewer during their introduction. These are included in Chapter 6: Interviewing with Hospitals. The answers provide a clear view of the unit and hospital and what to expect of the assignment. Not all these questions apply to every situation, but I hope they trigger ones that apply to your situation or are important to you.

HOSPITAL/UNIT DETAILS

- What is the name of the interviewer and their position?
- What is the location of the hospital?
- How many beds are there in the hospital?
- How many floors are there?
- What is the type of patient population?
- How many beds are there in the unit?
- What is the parking situation (ease and cost of parking)?
- What type of orientation is required (length of time, both hospital and unit orientation or just unit)?

STAFFING

- What is the nurse-to-patient ratio?
- Will I be asked to float?
- What shift are they looking to fill?
- Is overtime often available?
- Who will be scheduling me?
- Is it possible my shift will ever be canceled? How often?
- What would be the likelihood of extending the assignment?

WORK ENVIRONMENT

- What nursing management model do they use on the unit?
- How many travelers are currently working on the unit?
- What support staff are available (nurse aides, lab, techs RT, PT)?
- What is the computer charting system used?
- What is the required color of scrubs?

Profile Submission Journal Entry

Below is an example of how I setup the journal I referred to in Chapter 5 to keep up with which agency submitted my profile for which assignment. As you can see, I also include space to write answers to the questions to ask during the interview.

- Travel Agency Used
- Date of Submission
- Hospital
- Unit
- Shift
- Projected Start Date
- Time Off Requests

- Taxable Rate
- Overtime Rate
- Holiday Rate
- Call-Back Rate
- Housing Subsidy
- M & I Reimbursement

- Travel Reimbursement
- Other Reimbursement

Hospital Details

....

....

Staffing

....

....

Work Environment

....

....

....

Letter of Resignation

Below are the examples of letters of resignation I referred to in Chapter 7. You can find other models on the internet and templates included in your word processing program.

Hard Copy Example

Your Name
Your Address
Your City, State Zip Code
Your Phone Number
Your Email

Date
Name of Manager or Supervisor
Title
Organization
Address
City, State Zip Code

Dear Mr./Ms. (Last Name of Manager or Supervisor):

I would like to inform you that I am resigning from my position as (insert position title) for (insert hospital name), effective (insert date), to pursue travel nursing.

Thank you very much for the opportunities for professional and personal development you have provided me during the last (insert #) years. I have enjoyed working for the hospital and appreciate the support provided me during my tenure.

Sincerely,
Your Signature
Your Typed Name

Email Example

Subject Line: Resignation – Your Name

Dear Mr./Ms. (Last Name of Manager or Supervisor):

I would like to inform you that I am resigning from my position as (insert position title) for (insert hospital name), effective (insert date), to pursue travel nursing.

Thank you very much for the opportunities for professional and personal development you have provided me during the last (insert #) years. I have enjoyed working for the hospital and appreciate the support provided me during my tenure.

Best regards,
Your Name
Email
Phone

Assignment Housing Search

These are websites I have found over the years of searching for housing as a traveler. The ones discussed in Chapter 8 are the services I have used.

https://www.9flats.com/
https://www.airbnb.com/
https://www.corporatehousing.com/
https://www.corporatehousingbyowner.com/
https://www.craigslist.org/
https://www.furnishedfinder.com/
https://www.oakwood.com/
https://www.transplanthousing.com/
https://www.travelershaven.com/
https://www.vrbo.com/
https://zeusliving.com/

Facebook Groups

Travel Nursing: Places/Room for Rent
Gypsy Soul Travel Nurse Housing Options
Travel Nurse Housing Rentals by Landlords
Travel Nurse Housing-Pet Friendly
Traveling Nurse Housing

There are many more groups available based on specific locations.

https://www.allconnect.com/

All Connect is a service for determining cable, internet, and telephone service providers at your temporary housing, should you need to set these items up yourself.

Mail Services

If you have chosen to use mail forwarding or change of address with each assignment through the US Postal Service, you can complete the forwarding or change forms online at

https://www.usps.com/

Below are the websites of several providers of virtual mailbox service that allow you to receive, forward, pick up, shred, or discard mail and packages.

https://ipostal1.com/
https://www.virtualpostmail.com/
https://www.earthclassmail.com/
https://www.postscanmail.com/
https://www.anytimemailbox.com/
https://physicaladdress.com/

Car Shipping Companies/Brokers

For travelers flying to their assignment and shipping their vehicle, below are a few of the companies and brokers which I found in my past searches when considering shipping my vehicle.

http://www.waggonerstrucking.com/
https://roadrunnerautotransport.com/
https://www.autotransportdirect.com/
https://www.montway.com/
https://www.nationalautoshipping.com/
https://www.nationwideunitedautotransport.com/

Packing List

This is a generic list to help you have a conversation with the agency housing coordinator or landlord about what is included in the housing. This way, you know what you *need* to bring with you and what you can buy once you arrive at your assignment location. It should also trigger remembering items vital to you that need to make the journey too. Don't forget the following apps, if you need help with making a complete list: PackPoint, Travelers Checklist, Packtor, Packpal, and SmarterTravel are available options.

Bedroom

* Sheets
* Pillows
* Blankets, comforter/duvet
* Alarm clock
* Clothes hangers

Bathroom

* Towels
* Washcloths
* Shower curtain and hooks
* Trashcan
Hairdryer
Brush
Comb
Razor
Make-up
Toothbrush
Toothpaste

Kitchen

* Cooking utensils
* Dishes and glassware
* Silverware
* Pots and pans
* Dishtowels
* Potholders
* Coffeemaker/tea kettle
* Microwave
* Toaster
Crock-Pot
Food storage containers

Living Area

* TV
DVD/Blu-Ray player
Streaming device
Small radio or digital speaker
Gaming console

Home Cleaning

* Laundry basket
* Small vacuum

* Broom/dustpan
* Mop/bucket

Indicates items generally included with housing

Electronics

Cell phone
Camera
Camcorder
Laptop, tablet
Wi-Fi router, if not included
Printer
Batteries and chargers
Flashlight
E-reader

Clothing

Scrubs
Work Shoes
Dressy and casual clothes
Workout clothes
Sleepwear, bathrobe
Shoes
Sweaters
Coats (rain and winter)

Work Items

Stethoscope
Penlight
Workbag for all your nursing paraphernalia
Phone numbers for nurse manager, new facility and your recruiter
A copy of your travel nursing contract
First-day instructions
Timecards

Copies of nursing license, credentials, and documentation requested

Personal Items

Driver's license
Car registration and insurance papers
Social Security card
Major credit cards, debit cards
Personal photographs and mementos

Pet Parents

Food and water bowls
Carrier or crate
Leash
Collar
Harness
Medications
Toys
Food
Grooming necessities

Day Off Activities

Swimwear
Beach towel
Hiking Shoes
Bicycle
Musical instruments
Scuba gear
Skis (snow or water)
Rollerblades
Boat
Motorcycle
Jet ski

Whatever you need for fun!

The Healthcare Traveler Conference (TravCon)

TravCon started in 2008 and has grown into the largest single gathering of healthcare travelers in the world. TravCon is a non-profit educational organization, and all governing committee members are either current or former travelers or dedicated individuals working to promote healthcare traveling. It provides a unique opportunity for travelers to advance their education, network with other travelers, meet agency representatives, potentially land their next assignment, and earn CEs—all in a fun, low-pressure setting. Their mission centers on serving the needs of travel healthcare professionals through **community, knowledge and inspiration.**

Alright, now that the information from the website is out of the way, let me give you my first-hand experience with TravCon. The two-day conference is held in Las Vegas (my favorite destination) every year in September to allow travelers to plan time off. The conference offers all travelers—planning to travel, just starting out, and experienced—up-to-date information about the industry. Typical topics covered are:

- Am I Ready to Travel as a New Grad or Novice Clinician?
- Assignments Outside the Bedside
- RV Housing for Healthcare Travelers
- Safety and Self-Defense for Travelers
- Travel Assignments in Australia
- Traveler Taxes
- Traveling with Pets

Every year, the conference gets great keynote speakers. In 2019, I had front row seats for Nurse Blake, the Facebook and YouTube personality known for Banned4Life and Nurses Support Their Young. In 2017, ZDoggMD™, Dr. Zubin Damania, gave one of his great, unfiltered truth talks, like the ones that can be caught on Facebook, YouTube, and ZDoggMD™ website. There have been other big names over the years, making it well worth the trip. The conference offers stuff for the non-healthcare spouses/partners who come with their healthcare traveler, while the traveler is off learning and collecting continuing education credits. Also offered are pre-and post-conference trainings that include Newbie Boot Camp, which I highly recommend since you bought this book, if you can get out to Vegas in September. Other offerings include basic medical Spanish, CCRN review, TNCC review, and AWHONN certifications.

The best part of this conference is meeting other travelers, networking with healthcare travel agencies, and enjoying some trips (hiking, canoeing, rafting) and pool parties. Last, but not least, the conference has an after-party held at Drai's Beach Club and Night Club. My descriptions do not do justice to the learning and fun that occurs during TravCon, so I recommend visiting the conference website and the YouTube channel TravCon TV. You're bound to find something that will interest you enough to pack a bag and head for Vegas.

https://travcon.org/

Traveler Blogs, Websites and Podcasts

BLOGS & WEBSITES

- Bluepipes.com
- Escapees RV Club
- Nomadicare
- Off the Clock Nurse
- PanTravelers.org
- Passports & Preemies
- The Gypsy Nurse
- The Traveling Nurse
- Travel Nursing Newbies

PODCASTS

- Atlas All Access (Apple Podcast)
- Bedside Manners: Travel Nursing Unhinged (Spotify)
- Behind the Scrubs (Spotify)
- Don't Stop RVing (Spotify)
- New Medical Nomads (Stitcher)
- The Happy Traveler (Apple Podcast)
- The Truth About Travel Nursing (Spotify)
- Travel Nurse Insiders (Spotify)
- Travel Nursing and Allied Life (Spotify)
- Travel Nursing Classroom (Stitcher)

Glossary

Assignment: The location (hospital, long-term acute care facility, nursing home) of a contract, including the duration of the initial contract and all contract extensions before moving to a new location (used interchangeably with contract, but not the same.) Chapter 1

Compact License, or Nurse Licensure Compact (NLC): A multistate license allowing the holder to practice nursing in the holder's home state and any state that has implemented Nurse Licensure Compact legislation. Chapter 2

Contract: A signed agreement between a traveler, the travel nurse agency, and the employing facility. It establishes the rights and responsibilities of all parties. It includes wages (regular, holiday, overtime, and call-back), employment duration, schedule (shift and hours per week), time-off requests, reimbursements to be provided, and other benefits. Chapter 7

Contract Extension: An addendum to the original contract of an assignment upon completing the initial contract terms. The addendum will stipulate any changes to wages (regular, holiday, overtime, and call-back), schedule (shift and hours per week), reimbursements, and other benefits. It will include the new end date of employment and time-off requests. Chapter 12

Guaranteed Hours Contract: A signed agreement between a traveler, the travel nurse agency, and the employing facility ensuring the traveler will receive hourly wages for hours or shifts canceled by the facility during the duration of employment up to the weekly hours stipulated in the agreement. The agreement usually stipulates the traveler may be canceled up to 36 hours per contract without hourly wage reimbursement (industry standard). This is a benefit provided to the traveler funded from the pay package's agency fees (Chapter 3). Chapter 7

License Endorsement: The permission to work in another jurisdiction for nurses already licensed to work within the US. This is for the non-compact (single) state license holder to practice nursing outside of the current state of licensure. Chapter 2

Managed Service Provider (MSP): A company responsible for managing an organization's contingent workforce. These companies may use a VMS application platform to provide their managing services. Chapter 3

Non-billable Orientation Hours: The hours spent by the contract hospital to orient a traveler. These hours are not paid by the hospital but the agency. The agency must "eat" this cost because, as a traveler, you are still paid your taxable hourly wage by the agency. This is a benefit to the traveler funded by the agency fees. Chapter 3

Nursys®: A national database for verification of nurse licensure, discipline, and practice privileges for RNs, LPN/VNs, and

APRNs licensed in participating jurisdictions, including all states in the NLC. Chapter 2

Profile: A collection of documents submitted to hospitals for evaluation and consideration for an offer of an assignment. The documents included are a résumé or application, nursing license(s), BLS/ACLS/PALS card(s), skills checklist(s), certification(s) information, and vaccination records. Chapter 2

Recruiter: An agency employee responsible for filling travel nurse vacancies. They are also responsible for reviewing a candidate's job experience, negotiating pay packages, and placing candidates in agreeable employment positions. Chapter 4

Referral Bonuses: An incentive provided by the agency to motivate employees to recruit candidates from within their networks to work for the agency. The referral bonus is granted once the candidate is hired and remains with the agency for a predetermined amount of time. This is one of the benefits to travelers funded by the agency fees (Chapter 3). The bonus is a taxed item.

Travel Nurse Agency: A company responsible for finding and supplying nurses who travel to work in temporary nursing positions in hospitals, long-term acute care facilities, clinics, and nursing homes. Chapter 4

Vendor Management System (VMS): An application platform for an organization to oversee and obtain staffing services and outside contracts or contingent labor. Chapter 3

Index

About the Author

CONSTANCE BUCCERE, MSN, RN, CCRN-CMC-CSC, IS A critical care nurse, nurse educator, and writer. She has spent the last ten years in the travel healthcare industry. During that time, she earned a master's in nursing education from the University of Alabama at Birmingham and specialty certifications in critical care, cardiovascular medicine, and cardiovascular surgery, placing her among the top five percent of registered nurses in the US. She is a member of Sigma Theta Tau International Honor Society of Nursing and the American Association of Critical-Care Nurses.

In 2011, Constance co-authored *Hardwiring Best Practice Stroke Care* for presentation at the American Nurses Credentialing Center National Magnet Conference®. In the spring of 2015, she was awarded 'Preceptor of the Year' by Our Lady of the Lake Regional Medical Center for her work training undergraduate and new hire nurses in the cardiovascular intensive care unit and her contributions to developing a critical care course for the facility. Constance continues to work as a travel nurse in the cardiovascular-cardiothoracic intensive care specialty and creates nursing content for online continuing education providers.

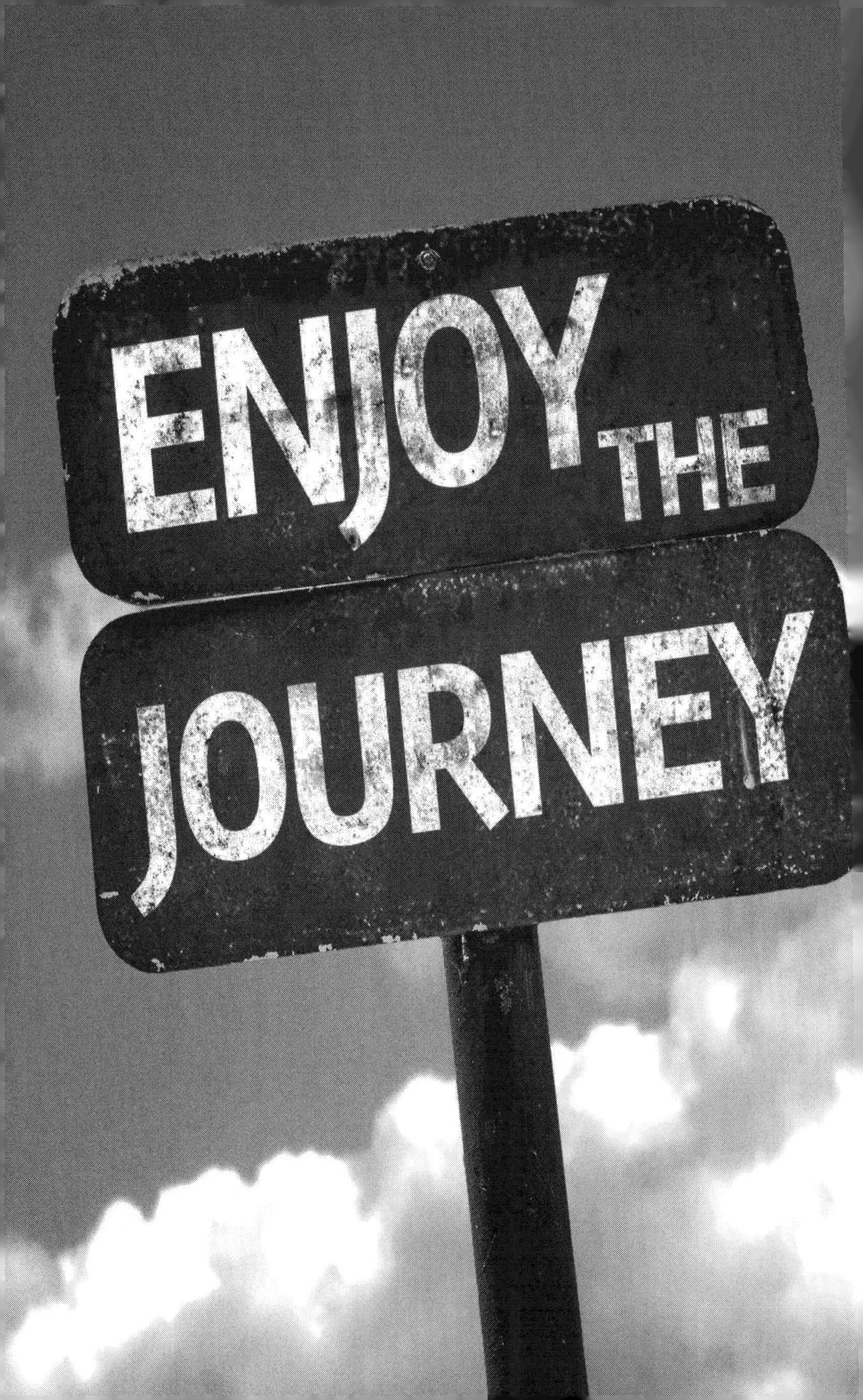
ENJOY THE
JOURNEY

Made in the USA
Monee, IL
16 October 2024

68078396R00111